Pierre Bonnard

9 **Marguerite** 1892

Royal Academy of Arts

Winter Exhibition 1966

1867-1947 **Pierre Bonnard**

Royal Academy of Arts in London 1966

List of Contributors

Aberdeen Art Gallery

Dr. Ing. Willi Aebi

Musée Toulouse-Lautrec, Albi

Art Properties, Inc.

Ashmolean Museum, Oxford

Baltimore Museum of Art

Barber Institute of Fine Arts, the University of Birmingham

Kunstmuseum, Basle

Galerie Beyeler, Basle

Maître A. Bellier

Mme Bellier

Bernheim-Jeune, Paris

Cecil G. Bernstein, Esq.

Museum of Fine Arts, Boston

Mme Ph. Boulart

Mesdemoiselles Bowers

Kunsthalle, Bremen

Musées Royaux des Beaux-Arts de Belgique, Brussels

Mrs. Charlotte Bührle

National Museum of Wales, Cardiff

Mr. Walter P. Chrysler, Jr.

Cleveland Museum of Art

Charles Clore, Esq.

R. M. Coode, Esq.

Courtauld Institute Galleries (Courtauld Collection and Fry Collection)

Monsieur Henri Decoin

Municipal Gallery of Modern Art, Dublin

Dr. Jacques Dupont

National Gallery of Scotland, Edinburgh

Monsieur J.-C. Eger

Mrs. Charles W. Engelhard

Mrs. Walter Feilchenfeldt

R. R. Figgis, Esq.

Fogg Art Museum, Harvard University, Cambridge, Mass.

Mr. Henry Ford II

Mrs. Nikolas Ghika

Glasgow Museums and Art Galleries

Lady Glenconner

Konstmuseum, Gothenburg

Mrs. Frank Jay Gould

Fairfax Hall, Esq.

Kunsthalle, Hamburg

Mrs. Maurice Harris

Mr. and Mrs. Henry J. Heinz II

D. F. Hellings, Esq.

Sir Antony and Lady Hornby

Jeremy Hutchinson, Esq.

Frau Doktor L. Jaeggli-Hahnloser

Lady Jamieson

Dott. Emilio Jesi

Terence Kennedy, Esq.

Knoedler and Co. Ltd.

Dr. Jacques Ch. Koerfer

Mr. David Lloyd Kreeger

Edward Le Bas, Esq.

Leeds City Art Gallery

Collection Leten, Ghent

Cecil Lewis, Esq.

John Lowe, Esq.

Galerie Rosengart, Lucerne

S. Rosengart Collection, Lucerne

M. Aimé Maeght, Paris

Miriam, Lady Marks

National Gallery of Victoria, Melbourne

Mr. and Mrs. Paul Mellon

Galleria Civica d'Arte Moderna, Milan

Milwaukee Art Center

Collection Morgan-Snell, Paris

A. Morhange, Esq.

Mr. Hugo L. Moser

Dr. Fritz and Dr. Peter Nathan

Museum of Modern Art, New York

Schoneman Galleries Inc., New York

Stavros S. Niarchos, Esq.

Smith College Museum of Art, Northampton, U.S.A.

J. O'Hana, Esq.

H. F. Oppenheimer, Esq.

Nasjonalgalleriet, Oslo

Bibliothèque Nationale, Paris

Musée du Petit Palais, Paris

Musée National d'Art Moderne, Paris

Mrs. Oliver Parker

The Trustees of C. Maresco Pearce, Esq.

Mrs. Rosemary Peto

Philadelphia Museum of Art (Louis E. Stern Collection)

Lazarus Phillips, Esq.

Carnegie Institute, Museum of Art, Pittsburgh

The Hon. Mrs. A. Pleydell-Bouverie

Musée de Poitiers

A. J. McNeill Reid, Esq.

Mr. and Mrs. Emery Reves

Dr. H. M. Roland

Roland, Browse & Delbanco Gallery

The Earl of Rosslyn

Lord Sainsbury

Mr. and Mrs. R. J. Sainsbury

Musée de L'Annonciade, Saint-Tropez

The Hon. Peter Samuel

Herr Walther Scharf

Southampton Art Gallery

Stedelijk Museum, Amsterdam

Mr. and Mrs. Donald S. Stralem

Staatsgalerie, Stuttgart

Tate Gallery

Monsieur Claude Terrasse

Toledo Museum of Art

Mrs. Dudley Tooth

Art Gallery of Toronto

Galleria Internazionale d'Arte Moderna, Venice

Victoria and Albert Museum, London

Mrs. Irene Vogel

Marcus Wickam-Boynton, Esq.

Wildenstein Inc.

Sir Isaac Wolfson, Bart.

Leonard Wolfson, Esq.

Mr. and Mrs. Charles Zadok

Kunsthaus, Zurich

And the owners who wish to remain anonymous.

Preface

Only a tiny band of foreign painters have been elected Honorary Members of the Royal Academy, but among them we are especially proud to number Pierre Bonnard, who was elected on the nomination of Augustus John and by an overwhelming vote, on April 26th, 1940. The date is perhaps of some significance since it coincided not only with a crucial moment in the war but, with a phase when Bonnard's art was yet to be universally acclaimed.

Bonnard's successor as a Honorary Academician, André Dunoyer de Segonzac, was the subject of a retrospective exhibition in our Diploma Gallery in 1959 and among our Members there has always been the wish to see a great Bonnard Exhibition mounted at Burlington House. Until recently the long drawn out lawsuit about the inheritance of his estate made such a project virtually impracticable, since such a substantial part of his output had remained unsold at his death. Now, thanks to the efforts of Mr. Denys Sutton and the co-operation of many old friends of the artist, we have been able to realise our hopes on a scale far beyond what had ever been envisaged. This is the largest and most representative Bonnard Exhibition to be held anywhere in the world and it is especially rich in paintings from the artist's studio which have never previously been seen in public.

In making this display possible in London, the Royal Academy is greatly indebted to Mr. and Mrs. Charles Zadok, M. Charles Terrasse, M. Henri and M. Jean Dauberville, of Bernheim-Jeune, the Mlles Bowers, the Bibliothèque Nationale, Paris, and to the many other lenders whose names are recorded on a following page, as well as to those who have preferred to remain anonymous. I should like to record special thanks to M. Daniel Wildenstein, who has provided us with much information concerning the whereabouts of a number of major works.

Our warmest thanks are due to M. Charles Terrasse for help in various ways.

Our thanks also are due to Mr. John Rewald for permission to reproduce his chronology from a Museum of Modern Art catalogue.

Mr. Denys Sutton has given unstintingly of his expert knowledge, time and energy. He has laboured as a perfectionist both to provide London with an exhibition which will never be forgotten and to honour an artist of whom he writes with such insight in his introduction. He has also borne the drudgery of compiling the catalogue. In all his efforts he has been assisted by his wife, Cynthia Sutton. Our gratitude and the gratitude of every visitor is due to them both.

I also wish to acknowledge here the work of Mr. Gordon House, as designer of the catalogue.

Finally, I must emphasise that in the organisation of this project the Royal Academy has been faced with entirely unprecedented expenditure. Due to the recent sale-room prices of Bonnard's paintings, the insurance values of the works entrusted to our care exceed eight million pounds – far higher than the figure for any previous Winter Exhibition. We have also cast our net very wide, drawing in all from 14 countries, with correspondingly heavy costs of transport. For these reasons our ordinary price of admission has for the first time been raised to what would normally be charged in other European capitals for an exhibition of this magnitude. It is too often forgotten that the large loan exhibitions held elsewhere in London are almost invariably subsidised – and this alone enables their price of admission to be kept at a quite uneconomic level. With insurance values and other costs at their current heights the future of Winter Exhibitions on the scale hitherto associated with Burlington House must now entirely depend on the public's response.

Charles Wheeler

General Information

**The exhibition opens on Thursday, January 6, 1966
and closes on Sunday, March 6, 1966**

Hours of admission
**Weekdays 10 am – 6 pm
Wednesdays until 8 pm
Sundays 2 pm – 6 pm**

Price of admission 10s   Sundays 5s

Illustrated catalogue 7s 6d (by post 9s 6d)

Reduced price admissions

Direct admission at the officially reduced rate of 5s for Students, Teachers accompanying parties, Members of Staff Associations, Working Men's or Girls' Clubs, or similar organisations can be obtained at the entrance to the Exhibition on production of a current student or membership card or other form of identification

Similar admission for members of Associations, etc, not issued with membership cards will be arranged if application is made in advance by the secretary or other responsible official of such an organisation to the Secretary, Royal Academy of Arts, Piccadilly, London, W1

Visitors are required to give up their sticks and umbrellas before entering the galleries; they must be left with the attendants at the Cloak Room in the Entrance Hall. The other attendants are strictly forbidden to take charge of anything

Invalids may obtain the use of a wheeled chair during certain hours, without charge, by previous arrangement with the Secretary, to whom application should be made for the necessary order

The Restaurant
(Fully Licensed)

Under the management of
Messrs. Ring & Brymer, Ltd
is open for

Morning Coffee and Light Refreshments	**10 to 11.30 am**
Luncheon	**12 noon to 2.30 pm**
Afternoon Tea	**3 pm to 5.30 pm**

The Restaurant is reached by the staircase from the Large South Room

253 **Portrait of the Artist** 1945

Pierre Bonnard

by Denys Sutton

Pierre Bonnard's contribution as the most important 'pure painter' of his generation has now become more widely and generously recognised. In fact, he may be considered as an heir to the grand tradition of the sixteenth century Venetians and to such more recent masters of emotive colour as Delacroix, Gauguin and Odilon Redon. Yet it would be a grave error to fall into the trap of assessing his achievement almost exclusively in terms of those later pictures in which colour assumed such magical intensity. This final phase can only be properly comprehended when it is related to his whole development. At all stages of his long and fertile career, Bonnard was an inventive artist and each stage in his evolution possesses its own particular quality.

Bonnard is in some ways a deceptive artist. Thus, his experiments, which were carried out relatively discreetly, are more radical and surprising than might be realised at first sight. They form the adventures of an artist who was ever eager to respond to the unexpected; his was a wandering eye, and, as Degas so well said, he cherished the accidental. Also, he considered that it was the artist's prerogative to embellish his subject matter and, in this respect, he never forgot Renoir's words to him that he excelled as a painter of charm. At all times, indeed, he was ready to explore any technique or style susceptible of furthering his artistic aims.

The exuberance which forms so congenial a part of his painting was reserved for his art alone. His life itself was passed in relative obscurity. He moved between Paris and Vernon in the early days and then between Paris and Le Cannet in the South of France. As a young man he travelled a certain amount, visiting England, Holland, Germany, Italy and Spain and in the 1920s he went to the United States. No legend can be prized out of his life story. It is true, of course, that his existence with Maria Boursin, who called herself 'Marthe de Méligny', was not without complications. He had met this attractive girl 'with the wildness of a bird' in 1894 when she was sixteen. They lived together for a long time and then married; and she served as the model for many of his pictures. She had a passion for brightly coloured clothes and for personal cleanliness but with age she succumbed to neurasthenia and became a recluse. In the 1930s, for instance, the German Maecenas Count Harry Kessler recounts how she would not receive anyone at home. Despite such handicaps Bonnard was devoted to her.

Although Bonnard had a circle of close friends, which included Octave Mirbeau, Besson, Jarry and Werth and a number of artists, he was a quiet and shy man. So much is made clear from the various photographs which were taken of him during his lifetime. Moreover, the remarkable series of *Self-Portraits* which he painted in later years, several of which are in this exhibition (Nos. 246, 253, 255), bring out his loneliness and fastidiousness. They also point to that quizzical and ironic trait in his nature which is revealed so frequently in his art.

Yet Bonnard was in no way a *naïf* person; on the contrary, he possessed a sophisticated intelligence. The occasional and acute remarks which he made about the art of painting, for instance, those reported by his nephew Charles

Terrasse or by Angèle Lamotte, indicate that he had given a great deal of thought not only to his own work but to earlier art. Bonnard was a cultivated man; he saw himself as the successor to a tradition; but, for all that, he was not hidebound and certainly no doctrinaire.

His eye was extraordinarily pure. His earliest paintings are either simple flower pieces (No. 1) or else landscapes which depict the countryside in the Isère (No. 2) where his family owned a house. These works reveal an eye for pictorial 'values' which suggest some affinity with Corot's small sketches. Bonnard was soon to come into close contact with some of the most interesting men of his generation. By a happy chance his companions at the Académie Julian in the late 1880s included not only some of the most congenial, but some of the most gifted men, of his time. It was singularly fortunate that he should have become there such an intimate friend of Vuillard and Maurice Denis; all three had so much in common. Like these young artists he became aware of the theory of expressive painting which was being propagated by Gauguin at Pont-Aven in 1888 and of which Sérusier had provided a taste in his famous little panel, *Le Talisman*. This picture, incidentally, can now be seen in the Pont-Aven exhibition at the Tate Gallery.

Bonnard grew up during a complex and exciting period, the *fin de siècle*, and his art was more deeply affected by many of the ideas then current than is sometimes believed. This did not stop him from going his own way; for instance, when he and his friends clubbed together to acquire a picture by Gauguin which they would each borrow, he neglected to take his turn. Moreover, whereas Sérusier or Denis, to mention just two of the circle, were fascinated by the esoteric lore enshrined in Edmond Schuré's book *Les Initiés*, Bonnard cared not a jot about such matters. His tastes none the less were exotic and they led him to become a keen admirer of Japanese prints.

Admiration for these vivid and elegant works, as hardly requires emphasising, was by no means new in France. Earlier on Théodore Rousseau and J. F. Millet and then Degas and Gauguin had been deeply attracted by Japanese prints and so, for that matter, had Whistler. Bonnard was the one artist whose temperament and style brought him the closest to the principles of Japanese art. It was hardly surprising that he earned for himself the nickname of 'the very Japanese Nabi'. He was especially drawn to the *mise-en-page* of the Japanese print and his representation of women in his early pictures recalls those in the prints of Utamaro. This trait may be observed in the *Partie de Croquet*, 1892 (No. 10); at the same time this whimsical picture – as well as the four enchanting panels for a screen painter in 1891 (No. 7) – express his delight in gaily coloured dress materials. This quirk of Bonnard's was specially noticed by Thadée Natanson. Indeed, Bonnard's interest in pretty materials frequently appears in his early works, and it is possible that he may have looked at the contemporary textile designs made by William Morris. There is perhaps an echo of Pre-Raphaelite sensibility in his charming little picture of girl surrounded by a flowered border of 1892 (No. 9).

It is not too fanciful to notice an English connexion in the many paintings and drawings he made of children in these years. They are amongst his more appealing and spontaneous creations, attesting to his deep affection for children. Here he was in step with his contemporaries. The interest in children's books was relatively widespread in Paris during the last years of the nineteenth century and books designed by Kate Greenaway and Randall Caldecott were exhibited there. Gauguin, indeed, had even gone so far as to

256 **Sketch for the Poster, France Champagne** 1889

278 **J'ai tout donné pour rien** *c.* 1899

tell the English artist, A. S. Hartrick, in 1886 of his admiration for Caldecott's books.

This interest was partly occasioned by the widespread desire to revitalise art by means of a return to primitive sources. The *avant-garde*, which were excited by the Wagnerian concept of a *Gesamtkunst*, believed that the arts should be more closely connected and, in particular, they championed a strong relationship between the fine and the applied arts. In 1892, Maurice Denis, who in many ways was spokesman for the group, published an influential article on this theme. Under this dispensation, it became perfectly natural for Bonnard to adapt his admiration for Japanese art for practical purposes and during the 1890s he designed a number of screens, indicative of his admiration for a typical Oriental genre. This exhibition includes the famous lithograph screen (No. 341) which reveals the effective way in which the artist combined a Japanese handling of space with a very Parisian sense of chic.

Bonnard's flair for decoration made him one of the first true artists of the time to be attracted by poster design – a further illustration of the way in which the fine arts could be employed for practical purposes. His father had wished him to enter the legal profession but Bonnard was lucky enough to escape from his job when commissioned to design a poster for 'La France Champagne' (No. 303), one of the sketches (No. 256) for which is also on view here. This jolly poster indicates that, in the same way as Seurat, he was intrigued by the frolicsome art of Jules Chéret. Bonnard is reputed to have introduced Toulouse-Lautrec, only three years his senior, to the printer Ancourt and thus to have started him on his career as a poster artist. However, this is denied by Natanson. In any event, Lautrec championed the work both of Bonnard and Vuillard and some connexion is to be found between their sketchy handling of paint and their subject matter. Nevertheless, although attracted by night life, Bonnard's interpretation of Montmartre is gentler than Lautrec's. In the same way as this artist, however, he produced a number of original and enchanting lithographs. His technique as a painter owed much to his work in this genre and he once told André Suares that 'I learned much about painting proper from making lithographs in colour, when one has to establish relations between tones by ringing the changes on only four or five colours, superimposed or juxtaposed, one makes a host of discoveries'.

During the 1890s and 1900s, Bonnard tried his hand at various decorative projects. In addition to the screens, he made a table centre which was cast in bronze (now in the Musée d'Art Moderne, Paris); this has certain affinities with Rodin's bronzes. In 1895, the well known dealer in Japanese art, S. Bing, commissioned him to execute a design, *Maternité*, for a stained glass window which was carried out by Tiffany and shown at the Société Nationale (Champs de Mars). He is also reported to have designed a 'very Nabique desk' for Thadée Natanson, the editor of *La Revue Blanche*, which was especially equipped with a recess to accommodate the art critic's generous stomach.

Enough has been said to indicate that Bonnard was temperamentally an exponent of the one style which was the most dominant and all embracing of the period – Art Nouveau. The decorative qualities in his paintings in which a linear rhythm covers the surface with arabesques of paint, in a way reminiscent of the waves of Hokushai or Monet, are characteristic of this movement. The question remains to be asked whether some of his later work still remained imbued with an Art Nouveau spirit; his desire to fill the whole composition with passages of paint, which was so marked in the final works, certainly revealed a *horor vacui* in keeping with one of its main principles.

His gifts as a decorator are equally well shown in the various book illustrations he made in the 1890s and 1900s. For instance, he decorated the musical scores of his brother-in-law Claude Terrasse (No. 348) and contributed illustrations to *La Revue Blanche*, notably of Peter Nansen's tender little novel *Marie* (No. 349). In the 1900s he was asked by Ambroise Vollard to illustrate Verlaine's *Parallèlement* (No. 351) and his delicious drawings present a number of comparisons with his paintings. It was characteristic of his ingenuity and initiative that in this sumptuous undertaking the lithographs are conceived as forming an integral part of the text; they possess singular grace and vivacity.

Bonnard was attracted by the stage as well. Together with Vuillard and Maurice Denis he shared, in 1890, a studio at 28 rue Pigalle with Lugné-Poë, who left some vivid sketches of Bonnard in his memoirs at this time. Bonnard quickly responded to stage work, designing programmes and painting scenery. His experience as a stage designer, about which little is known in detail, was important for his development and the arrangement of some of his compositions probably owe something to the theatre.

One of Bonnard's most unusual early pictures is the *Les Poupées* (No. 181) of 1895 and it reminds us that a year later he was concerned in the presentation of Jarry's *Ubu Roi* at the Théâtre de l'Oeuvre and he collaborated with Terrasse in making puppets for the Théâtre des Pantins. It would be fascinating to know more about the reasons which prompted Bonnard and some of his friends to be so keen on the puppet theatre. Did they believe, as did Kleist, that the puppet theatre could be a more effective translator of an author's intentions than an actor? A concern with puppets was in the air. In 1892 Oscar Wilde declared that 'There are many advantages in puppets. They never argue. They have no crude views about art. They have no private lives . . . They recognise the presiding intellect of the dramatist, and have never been known to ask for their parts to be written up. They are admirably docile, and have no personalities at all'. These remarks were made apropos a production of the *Tempest* which he had seen in Paris at Maurice Bouchor's Petit Théâtre des Marionettes in the Galerie Vivienne.

276   **Etude de Nu sur un Lit** *c.* 1899

Antoine Terrasse has also suggested that the 'Chinese shadow theatre' may have exerted some influence on Bonnard at this period.

In any event, the idea of showing figures in silhouette fascinated Bonnard, as much as it did Vuillard, and this approach may be seen in a number of his lithographs as well as in *Chez la Brodeuse* (No. 34). No doubt the two men were equally intrigued by Redon's black chalk drawings, and Bonnard admired this artist's combination of 'a very pure *matière* and a mysterious expression'. Redon also made a portrait of him. Bonnard was no less an admirer of Seurat as Natanson points out; and he would have heard much about this artist from Félix Fénéon, who became the editorial secretary of *La Revue Blanche*, a magazine for which Bonnard designed a most attractive poster in 1894 (No. 328).

Bonnard's independence during the 1890s was shown by the fact that, although Gauguin had made the younger artists acutely aware of the appeal of bright colour, the tonalities in the younger painter's pictures are frequently dark. In this respect, he differed from his friend Vuillard whose colour was higher in key and who gave his compositions a greater dynamism. However, the two men were closely related in their mutual love of the intimist approach.

This particular style, which was endorsed by such writers as Jean Dolent, Gustave Geffroy and Charles Morice, was one of the principal currents of the 1890s. J. E. Blanche has rightly maintained that this style stemmed from the Dutch masters of the seventeenth century and from Chardin, whose work, incidentally, influenced Matisse in his younger days. This observant painter-writer pointed out that there was 'hardly a house without a small, modest canvas, representing a corner of a nursery, a dining room, old furniture used by years of human contact. These were pictures which had as their subject matter scenes such as breakfasts, evenings spent round the lamp, home work, or the plucking of vegetables in the kitchen. There were those façades of old provincial buildings or those gardens planted with flowers by monsieur le curé painted at the poetical hour of twilight which Le Sidaner or René-Xavier Prinet rendered so charmingly or movingly for those who visited the Galerie George Petit'. This was a genre, in different ways, which had been taken up by Bonvin and Ribot, Van Gogh and Cézanne, Carrière and Laprade; and it also attracted a painter like Sickert whose work was admired by Bonnard. He gave his own twist to such subjects by bringing out the plays of perspective, which could be found in a table, thereby announcing some of his later preoccupations, and by emphasising the wonderment of a child when facing ordinary things. It was a quality which Bonnard himself sought to capture.

He was not only the painter of the domestic interior but the poet of the Parisian scene. Of course, he was not the first artist to have painted the city and Corot, Lépine, Renoir and Pissarro, not to forget more illustrative artists such as Beraud, Luigi Loir and Raffaëlli had done so before him. Yet he struck what was virtually a new note. He adapted the intimist approach to the street scene, finding his themes in girls walking along the Boulevards, lamps at night in the Place Blanche or Place Pigalle or the silhouettes of a fiacre (shades of Yvette Guilbert!) Some connexion may be noted here with the small watercolours and lithographs which Whistler made of the Paris streets, although their technique is very different.

In his Parisian pictures Bonnard assumed the role of a spectator. As a young man he had admitted his pleasure at looking at the street scenes and in noting down what he saw; his sketch-books stress his delight in drawing. The vivacity found in these sketches is also present in his oils. There is, too, an ironic touch about them which recalls the plays of Tristan Bernard and Porto-Riche. It is as if he was hinting at the theory of the absurd which is found in the Jarry's *Ubu Roi*. It was André Mellerio who noted that in such works Bonnard knew how to capture, without making the scene lose its velvety quality, the delicate kaleidoscope and always unexpected display of fireworks which constitute Paris. His was the vision of a complicated civilisation engaged in ceaseless movement where everything has its note of colour and profits from it. Again, as Gustave Geffroy pointed out 'no one is quicker than Bonnard to seize the look of our Parisian streets, the silhouette of a passer by and the patch of colour which stands out in the metropolitan mist. His pencil is never still, quick and supple as a monkey, it seizes on all the momentary phenomena of the street, even the most fugitive glances are caught and set down.'

Bonnard's vision of Paris was essentially one of a petit bourgeois world. It was an interpretation revealed in his celebrated series of lithographs *Quelque Vues de Paris* which he made in 1895. In these brilliant examples of the lithographer's skill a gossamer touch is combined with receptivity to the interplay of rectangles and of empty spaces. There is also present in a print such as *Maison dans la cour* (No. 267) and in the *Roof Tops* (No. 25) an affinity with Vermeer's *View of Delft* which, as hardly requires emphasis, also appealed to Whistler and Proust. (Incidentally, Bonnard is recorded as having visited the salon of the Princess Bibesco.) As a painter of townscape, Bonnard may also be placed in a tradition which embraced not only Vermeer but Sanraedem; once again the Dutch component in French art is stressed.

Bonnard had a great sense of fun. This was signalled out, in his early days, by Lugné-Poë, who noted that he was 'the humorist amongst us. His nonchalant gaiety and good humour overflowed into his paintings, whose decorative quality at that time had a satirical quality which they lost later on'. Bonnard's satirical spirit, although never pushed to extremes, brought him close to the men who worked for *La Revue Blanche*. They shared his ironic view of life, and it was perhaps characteristic of Bonnard's own humorous attitude that he should have painted especially entertaining portraits of Thadée Natanson

259 **Deux Nus** *c.* 1890   286 **Deux Têtes de Femmes**   283 **Sketch for a Poster for**
                                        c. 1920   **Les Ballets Russe** 1914

(No. 49) and of his charming wife Misia (Nos. 44, 77) who later on married
Edwards, the newspaper proprietor, and then the painter J. M. Sert. Although
Lugné-Poë suggests that it was only in his youth that his sense of humour
flourished, this is hardly borne out by the later pictures.

La Revue Blanche itself devoted a considerable amount of space to foreign
literature, including Scandinavian. For a man of letters like Gustave Kahn,
Scandinavian writing possessed that intimism which in his view provided
a necessary corrective to the French love of rhetoric and their inborn
romanticism. Bonnard, as already mentioned, contributed illustrations of
Nansen's *Marie* to the magazine and executed scenery for Ibsen's *Rosmersholm*.
It would be interesting to determine if he was at all influenced by Munch's
famous print *The Kiss* of 1895 when he painted the famous *Man and Woman* of
1899 in the Musée d'Art Moderne, Paris. There is a certain affinity to be
detected between their subject matter, though Bonnard's treatment was more
subtle. The influence may also have gone from Bonnard to Munch as the
figure of the man in the latter's picture *The Death of Marat*, of 1905-1927, in the
Munch Museum, Oslo, recalls one of the French artist's nudes.

In the late 1890s and during the 1900s, Bonnard began to experiment with one
of his favourite themes – the painting of nudes. This particular approach,
gentle and observant, is admirably displayed in the two versions of *L'Indolente*
(Nos. 40, 41) and it is pertinent to observe that the description of the one in the
Musée d'Art Moderne, Paris, given by Natanson indicates that it has darkened
considerably over the years. Bonnard's eroticism was refined and, in a way,
obsessional; he contemplated and caressed his nudes, as if they were cats,
fastening on the twist of a leg or the curve of an arm. He could be illustrating
a novel by Colette – and his girls often have the promise of adolescence.
Yet he never indulged in the obvious salaciousness of a Félicien Rops.

Bonnard's love of charm for its own sake, which Renoir commended, meant
that he shut his eyes to the seamier sides of Parisian night life. For him *la belle
époque* really was *la belle époque*. Thus, he favoured those tender little midinettes
who turn up so often in the pages of *La Vie Parisienne* and who haunted the
imagination of the Edwardian boulevardier. At the same time, just as much as

he avoided depicting the whores of Lautrec so he avoided those symbols of pneumatic bliss painted by Renoir in the later years.

Although in some of his pictures of nudes, such as the *Nu contre Jour* (No. 83), the composition remains crowded, he began at this stage to seek a more simplified conception of the picture space. He would place the figure in a studio, against a bare background and, when necessary, almost deform the contours, as in the two unusual pictures from Gothenburg (Nos. 57, 58). There seems little doubt, indeed, that at about this time, he looked attentively at Degas's nudes which he could have seen either at the eighth Impressionist exhibition at Durand-Ruel's in 1886 or else in this firm's stock. The relationship is underlined in the brilliant *Nu dans un tub* (No. 102) of 1912. However, he did not aim at presenting the figure as if it was a sculptural block, as did Degas; he sought to harmonise the colour relationship between the figure and the background. Light was gently filtered over the composition, and in a way reminiscent of Corot, although the tones are different; he bathed the picture in atmosphere. His luminism was employed so as to establish the figure in space but not so as to disturb the overall pattern. This delight in playing with light constituted one of the chief components of his style at this period just as, later on, he made much of the plays afforded by perspective. Thadée Natanson, in writing about his exhibition at Durand-Ruel's in 1899 said: 'He has the gift, distinctive of the truly great of catalysing all the ambient light, rarefying it, toning it down to the exquisite penumbra of the late evening or the muted radiance of an *Interior*. Sometimes when the fancy takes him as in his *Landscape in Normandy* he floods the scene with sunlight but sometimes he makes the light emanate, golden, all pervasive, from the sheets encircling a young woman's body dappled with vagrant gleams.'

The 1900s witnessed a considerable expansion in Bonnard's subject matter. He had painted landscapes as a young man, including the unusual panoramic view of 1894 (No. 12) which foreshadows many of the later pictures. Now he began to move outside Paris, forming the habit of visiting L'Etang-la-Ville, nearby where K. X. Roussel and Maurice Denis lived and, finally, just before the first world war, he took a house at Vernon. He called this 'Ma Roulotte', thus commemorating his passion for wandering about in a car. This retreat to the countryside occasioned an increasing number of landscapes, which were marked by bolder colour and a vigorous use of impasto. The variety of his style in the late 1900s, may also be observed in a picture such as *Sur le Yacht* (No. 66), 1906, which emphasises his fascination with unusual angles of vision.

Until 1910 Bonnard had mainly painted landscape in Northern France but in that year he discovered the Mediterranean. From then onwards he drew inspiration from this congenial district. He wrote to his mother about his visit there 'the Midi is extremely seductive and in fact I have had an experience akin to the thousand and one nights; the sea, the yellow walls, the reflections which are as coloured as the light effects'. The Mediterranean meant much to him and for a variety of reasons. It was a natural place for an artist to exploit a sense of colour, and it was also a part of the world where the classical past seemed especially relevant. He drew on the Mediterranean for his decorative paintings; in these, so Denis reported, 'he wished to start with a fragment, without any precise idea of nature. Nature had to be found afterwards or during the course of execution'.

Like his friends Vuillard and Denis, Bonnard was intimately concerned with the revival of decorative painting which occurred during the 1900s. Although he was never as active in this direction as Vuillard, who painted the famous decorations for Alexandre Natanson and Claude Anet, and Roussel who engaged in such projects all his life, Bonnard painted a number of important large-scale works in this genre. These include the four decorations for the Salon of Misia Godebska, which were executed just after she had left Natanson. In these idyllic pictures (one of which is on view No. 91) decorative motives are blended and enclosed within a border, and here the arabesque so favoured by Debussy in music, triumphs; and, as John Rewald so rightly said, 'they suggest a charming fairy tale told with an enchanted brush'. In 1911 he painted a set of decorations for the Russian collector Morosoff, for whom Roussel also worked. A sketch for the right-hand portion of this decoration is in the exhibition (No. 98). Later between 1916 and 1920 he produced a number of decorative paintings, including *Monuments* (No. 158) in which a classical note is sounded.

The decorations painted for Misia Godebska indicate that Bonnard was a follower of that grand tradition of French art which had produced Le Brun and Boucher, as well as the other designers of Gobelins tapestries. In this connexion, it is worth recalling that a taste for French eighteenth century art was widespread in the 1900s. However, it would be necessary to know more about Bonnard's artistic interests in order to grasp the extent to which he had consciously studied eighteenth century French tapestries. What deserves to be stressed is that these essays in large-scale decorative painting enabled him to relate the fine to the applied arts, thus achieving one of the aims of the Art Nouveau artists. In seeing such works, it is easy to understand how it was that Guillaume Apollinaire could say that we 'find once again in his art that mysterious liveliness which is so typical of the eighteenth century'.

Bonnard's enthusiasm for the Mediterranean was due to his liking for the South of France; it may equally well be explained in terms of his intellectual conceptions. His admiration for Greek literature and thought was considerable, as, for that matter, was Roussel's. It was typical of Bonnard that he should have responded so well to Vollard's invitation to illustrate Longus's *Daphnis et Chloé* (No. 80) and, characteristically, he made his illustrations so that they seem timeless; they present a lyrical love affair *par excellence*. His classicism was in tune with a trend of the age. For instance, in 1891 Moréas had published a manifesto in *Le Figaro* announcing the birth of the *école romane* and calling for a revival of the Graeco-Roman tradition; in his view, 'it renewed the "gallic" chain which had been broken by the Romantics and its Parnassian naturalist and symbolist heritage'. Another supporter of this trend, Charles Maurras, considered that *romanisme* formed a weapon against Romanticism and anarchy. Thus, there is a link, however loose, between the literary classicism of the 1890s and Bonnard's art. It is possibly significant that, according to Natanson, he adopted a nationalist view point in later years.

The classical temper of Bonnard's art is likewise stressed in a picture such as *Le Paon ou les Trois Grâces*, 1908 (No. 80) which has a specifically Antique theme. The women in this work look as if they had been sculpted by Maillol. Bonnard, in fact, painted a remarkably interesting *Hommage à Maillol* (No. 132). This classical note is apparent, as well, in some of his single nude studies where the pose of the figures seems to echo some Hellenistic sculpture. In his liking for classical sculpture Bonnard resembles the sixteenth-century Venetians and, like these painters, nothing Neo-Classical marked his treatment of the figure. It is not, of course, that he would make direct quotations from the

Antique after the manner of his hero Titian; he preferred a generalised impression. His admiration for Titian is evident in many of his pictures; both were painters of 'poesie' and both painted golden rosy-hued backgrounds to their pictures, as may be seen in Bonnard's wonderful *Abduction of Europa* (No. 138). This is one of the great mythological canvases of the twentieth century.

It never does to attempt to place Bonnard in one category alone. In his subtle way, he shows us a dozen different faces. He was a painter who most exquisitely conjured up a variety of moods – it was typical of him that he should have appreciated Mallarmé's poetry which he continually read. It is the essence of a poem such as the *Après midi d'un faune* that it does not present a slice from life but evokes a dream-like experience. Bonnard, as we have seen, painted during the 1910s a number of pictures in which mythology formed the subject matter. This choice of subject was dictated not by the need to enliven landscape by the introduction of figures but because such themes corresponded to his own dreams. He wove a web of colour which achieves a sort of Debussy-like mystery: he offers us his own version, as it were, of *Pelléas et Mélisande* translated from a Celtic into a Mediterranean idiom. From the 1910s onwards an emerging trend in his art was this dream-like evocation of experience, which once again arose from his desire to embellish life.

Bonnard, so his friends attest, was a rapid walker and his liking for swift movement was revealed in a number of his pictures of the 1900s, which almost take on something of Futurist dynamism. The little figures in his pictures move along as if worked by clockwork, or as if they were puppets. Shortly before the war, his painting took on a further staccato effect as the result, so it seems, of his visit to Hamburg in 1913. He and Vuillard had visited this city on a trip arranged by that fine connoisseur of modern French art, Alfred Lichtwark. On his arrival in Cologne he had confessed to Lichtwark that neither he nor Vuillard felt that they could paint in the German light but this feeling had disappeared once in Hamburg. Besides the *Portrait of Senator Stuhlmann* now in the Kunsthalle, he painted two effective views of the Alster (Nos. 111 and 112) which have a singular vibrancy of touch. It must have been as a result of this trip to Germany that he painted the well-known *Regatta* (No. 133) and the *Au jardin : conversation dans le parc* (No. 114). The dramatic handling of the figures and the richness of the colour in these pictures make it tempting to ask if he had seen some paintings by the German expressionist artists either in Hamburg or in Berlin. Bonnard would occasionally lower his guard and reveal that he had a sharp eye for human nature as in his famous picture *La Loge* (No. 82) or in the various and often very touching portraits of Marthe dating from the 1920s.

Bonnard always kept his eyes open. It would be fascinating to attempt to determine the debt which Matisse and he owed each other. They both delighted in the South of France and their pictures of views from open windows, either in this part of the world or elsewhere, such as the *Open Window* (No. 136) of 1918 have something in common. Both, too, surely owed a debt to Chinese, Persian or Near Eastern Art. It may well be, in fact, that the decoration found on the K'ang-Hsi porcelain pots, which were so favoured before 1914, counted for something in the artistic effects of these two men. Bonnard's early *Boules de Neige*, 1891 (No. 5) seems to suggest such a relationship. Matisse and Bonnard presumably visited the great Near Eastern exhibition held in Paris before the first world war, and the Orientalism in their painting follows a French tradition that has included Boucher and

293 **Paysage** *c.* 1925

Delacroix. indeed, Clive Bell once said that 'the design of a picture by Bonnard, like that of many Chinese pictures and Persian textiles seems to have been laid on the canvas as one might lay cautiously dry grass on some infinitely figured gauze'.

Bonnard and Matisse were akin in their experiments with space. Bonnard certainly admired this artist greatly and they were friends for many years. Although in a painting such as *The White Room* of 1930 (Grenoble), the space is clearly articulated in a way which bears some resemblance to Matisse's practice, he never really favoured the bare areas of rather opaque paint employed by his colleague. He was concerned to secure more complicated and intricate compositional devices such as the employment of different levels of perspective and to vary the transitions of tone from warm to cooler ones as in the *Dining Room in the Country*, of 1913 in the Minneapolis Museum. Bonnard was a virtuoso of painterly tricks who increasingly played with perspective. He found that he could secure an immense number of interesting effects by recourse to mirrors, and his irony came out in the use to which he put this device.

In about 1915 Bonnard became dissatisfied with his work and, as a result, conscious of his limitations. He made the position quite clear, saying 'I returned to school. I turned against all that had previously excited me, the colour which had attracted me. I had almost unconsciously sacrificed form to it but it is absolutely true that forms exist and that it is not possible either to arbitrarily reduce or transpose it. Thus it is vital to study it and after drawing there comes composition which should constitute an equilibrium: a picture which is satisfactorily composed is half made'. A stricter control of form may be observed in the series of nudes which date from then until the late 1920s, and, at the same time, some of his pen drawings were given a more expressive character. The emphasis was placed in such pictures on awkward gestures which enabled the artist to investigate unusual movements. It is also possible that in such pictures he may have remembered the studies by Degas which were included in this artist's sale of 1917.

The complexities of Bonnard's seemingly simple art may be noticed in the series of outdoor scenes such as Nos. 172, and 186, which he painted during the 1920s. These are pictures which conjure up a mysterious and allusive mood; the sitters are ordinary people and yet they are endowed with an air of surprise. This is no less true of the *Bol de Lait* (No. 143). Indeed, in a curious way, something of the post-war unrest appears in several of his paintings at this period. However, Bonnard did not achieve this mood by means of over-emphasis but by means of subtle changes in the positioning of the figures. This artist, who in 1912 had been called a *peintre déformateur*, showed his capacities in so many different ways. He had already indicated in the 1890s his ability to play with perspective and, in doing so, acknowledged a debt to Cézanne and Gauguin. But such experiments were not artificial; they provided a further illustration of the quizzical way in which he regarded the world and human beings. The problem of drawing, he said, was to represent masses and objects on a single plane. Our vision, he claimed, is both empirical and conventional. The point was that 'the painter's eye gives the objects a human value and reproduces things in a way that the human eyes see them. This vision is both variable and mobile'. In other words, Bonnard presented in his pictures a conflict between the real world, as it seems to be, and the world when transposed and interpreted by the artist. This interpretation was one which did not depart from figuration; however, he was not hostile to abstraction which he considered to be a legitimate department of art.

Bonnard's repertory of themes was more or less established by the mid-1920s. From then onwards he was faced with the problem of attempting to re-create his original vision in terms of an art which was still susceptible of extension and variation. In doing this, once again Bonnard the humorist showed his hand. The elliptical touches, the allusions, the sly digs even and the desire to present a maze, the key to which could only be found by the patient beholder – all these touches were natural for a man who had found himself in the world of Symbolism. What seems, at first sight, to be such a very exuberant art, was perhaps more introverted than might be believed. He began to exploit more fully his conception of colour, breaking up the image into a series of related passages. This is a process which may be compared with Picasso's experiments with linear design.

Bonnard was essentially a colourist who had the gift of being able to capture a variety of nuances in his pictures. His range in this respect is truly astonishing. Nevertheless, his artistic procedures rely more deeply on his drawings than is often realised. He drew constantly and it is now clear that many of his compositions originate in a pen or pencil sketch. Depending on the period in which they were done, such sketches are marked either by a charming whimsicality or else by an incisive character which indicates that the formal disposition of the composition was apparent to the artist before he translated his findings into paint.

Bonnard's admiration for Renoir is evident from the technique of many of his pictures, especially his flower pieces. Yet is was Claude Monet who meant the most to him. This artist lived at Giverny, near Vernon and Bonnard would often visit the old man. The touches of white impasto, which frequently occur in his paintings of the 1920s, as well as the arabesques formed by his colours, recall passages in Monet's paintings of water lilies of 1907 or his Irises of 1911. They came close together in another respect as well. Monet would watch the same scene at different hours of the day, registering his findings by means of subtle transformations in the picture surface. Bonnard adopted an analogous practice. He would not necessarily depict the subject according to different times of the day but he would return to the same theme continually and, like

Monet, he would often represent the composition on one plane. There is a relationship between them in the way in which Bonnard represented a woman in a bath tub giving the impression that she is floating on the surface like a water lily. Fortunately, this exhibition contains several pictures belonging to this group, ranging from the 1920s to the 1940s. (Nos. 177 and 240.) They emphasise the way in which Bonnard could invest his theme with infinite variety. It is no less fascinating to find that Bonnard made a small pencil drawing of a woman in a bath (No. 294); he is known to have painted a watercolour as well. It would prove an intriguing task to endeavour to work out the sequence of this series.

The question of Bonnard's chronology is a complex one. He would make some sketches in pencil or colour and then start work on a number of paintings simultaneously relying on his memory and constantly returning to retouch the surface. Owing to this practice it is by no means easy, and often quite impossible, to assign precise dates to many of the later pictures. This retouching might go on over a number of years and was the result of a desire to secure the maximum of colouristic effect. For, as he once said, 'A series of blobs which are linked by colour and which finally constitute the object, the piece on which the eye wanders uninterruptedly. The beauty of a piece of antique marble lies in the series of movements which the finger can make over it'. These small blocks of colour possess a jewel-like beauty which almost make them look like a mosaic, and there is little doubt that this technique exerted some influence on Nicolas de Staël. Bonnard, indeed, has greatly intrigued twentieth-century painters in recent years, and it is fascinating to find that the American artist Franz Kline felt that, when looking at a picture by him, you see him 'organising in front of you'.

The influence of the Japanese print maintained its hold on Bonnard in later years, especially in the series of views of St. Tropez, painted in the 1930s, in which a flat patterned effect is secured. Whereas, however, the composition in a Japanese print is divided by means of separate areas of colour, Bonnard achieved a tonal relationship in terms of an overall generalised colour, as in the celebrated picture from Albi (No. 236). This particular picture seems to offer a celebration to the sun, following the lines of Denis's article of 1906. In a sense, it might be said that Bonnard became a pantheist or *Unamiste* after the manner of a Jules Romains and, in doing so, he once again stressed his adherence to Mediterranean values.

His response to the sea is splendidly shown not only in such pictures which have the dancing quality of the Mediterranean but in his watercolours where Courbet's vision of infinity is translated into a never-never land of warm golden hues.

Bonnard's ingenuity remained constant. Even towards the end of his long life he continued to occupy himself with decorative projects. Thadée Natanson, for instance, reported that he had planned a decoration for a room in blue and yellow and he also painted a composition of St. Francis de Sales blessing the sick for the Church of Assy in Savoie. Then, too, he painted the intriguing *The Circus Horse* (No. 234). This, as Mr. J. T. Soby says, is 'opposite in spirit to the ghostly malignant stallion which looms through the window in Fuseli's famous *Nightmare* of 1782. Nevertheless, the effect is scarcely less obsessive, the buffoonery of the horse's absurdly elongated head unforgettable. Bonnard's image proves again that great humour can strike at our consciousness nearly as hard as terror'.

'Il faut mentir', he once said. His art illustrates his determination to create a pattern composed of calligraphy and colour and in which the final effects were shimmering and mysterious. He conceived of painting as 'a conflict between the initial idea, which is the sound one, and the varied and variable world of the object, of the motif which stimulated the first inspiration'. Thus, he considered that Titian was one of the greatest of all artists. 'By the seduction or the first idea the painter', he said, 'attains to the universal. It is the seduction which determines the choice of the motif and which corresponds exactly to the painting. If this seduction, if the first idea vanishes, all that remains is the motif, and object which invades and dominates the painter. From that moment on, he is no longer responsible for the picture. With some painters, Titian, for instance, this seduction is so powerful that it never forsakes them, even if for a long time they remain in contact with the object. I am very weak and it is difficult for me to control myself in front of the object.'

This search for seduction, this desire to maintain at fever pitch the moment of creation, and to prolong the thrill of rapture determine the character of Bonnard's art. The finest of his late pictures throb with intensity. He secured a magical transformation of the real world so that the interior of his studio or his garden at Le Cannet (No. 251) and the bowls of fruit and flowers that he loved, assume an infectious radiance. His rich orchestration of colour records a world which was on the verge of disappearing at the end of his life.

His paint has something almost edible about it, and it was hardly fortuitous that he so often painted meals and food on the table. These pictures symbolise the great French tradition of the *vie bourgeoise*. But there is nothing bourgeois about them. In his pictures, each section takes on an almost symbolical meaning, as in a Chinese bamboo painting; there is a content to be found in even his most evasive-seeming work. In his late *Self-Portrait* (No. 253) the artist, like some Oriental sage, peers at the world, fondly yet sadly. The meaning which he finally came to render is contained in the last picture he painted – the *Almond Tree* in the Musée d'Art Moderne, Paris and it is not a pessimistic one. He affirms his belief in the renewal of nature and, in a characteristically oblique manner, he opted for order, for balance and, of course, for continuity.

Chronology

1867
Oct. 13, Pierre Bonnard is born at Fontenay-aux-Roses, second child of Eugène Bonnard and Elizabeth Mertzdorff.

***c*. 1877**
Is put into a boarding school; goes to Lycée de Vanves and later to Lycées Louis-le-Grand and Charlemagne.

***c*. 1885**
After his baccalaureat studies law at the insistence of his father.

1888
Works at the Ecole des Beaux-Arts, competes unsuccessfully for the Prix de Rome. Interested in Japanese prints. Studies at the Académie Julian, Faubourg St. Denis, where he meets Denis, Vuillard, Ranson, Sérusier. In October Sérusier returns from Brittany and reveals Gauguin's art to his friends. The Nabis begin to gather regularly. Bonnard fails in oral law examinations, works in Government office.

1889
Lives 8 rue de Parme in Paris with his grandmother. Sells champagne poster for 100 francs and decides to become an artist. First studio rue Lechapelais in Batignolles quarter. Gauguin's exhibition at the Café Volpini is decisive factor in his evolution. 1889-90, military service at Bourgoin.

1890
Studio: 28 rue Pigalle with Vuillard and Denis later joined by Lugné-Poë. Bonnard's work is noticed by Lautrec. His sister, Andrée marries Claude Terrasse.

1891
Shows 5 canvases and 4 decorative panels, *Femmes au Jardin*, at the *Indépendants* and exhibits in the Autumn with his friends in Saint-Germain as well as at Le Barc de Boutteville's. Is noticed by the critic Geffroy. The *Revue Blanche* is founded by the Natanson brothers. Drawings by Bonnard and the other Nabis appear in 1891-92 in *La Vie Moderne*. Gauguin leaves for Tahiti.

1892
Shows 7 canvases at the *Indépendants*, also exhibits with his friends in Saint-Germain and at Le Barc de Boutteville's. His work is noticed by the critics Roger Marx and Aurier. Designs sets for the Théâtre d'Art.

1893
Studio: 65 rue de Douai. Exhibits at the *Indépendants* and in group show at Le Barc de Boutteville's. Contributes lithographs to the *Revue Blanche* and *L'Escarmouche*. Roussel marries Vuillard's sister. Illustrates Claude Terrasse's *Petites Scènes Familières au petit solfège* 1893-94, Lugné-Poë founds his Théâtre de l'Oeuvre. Vollard opens a small gallery rue Laffitte; Bonnard meets Vollard through Denis.

1894
Thadée Natanson buys paintings by Bonnard who exhibits at the *Indépendants* and in group show at Le Barc de Boutteville's.

1895
Tiffany shows at the Salon a series of stained glass windows, among them *Maternité* one after a design by Bonnard.

1896
First one-man show at Durand-Ruel's (49 paintings, some posters, lithographs, etc.). Claude Terrasse settles in Paris. With Terrasse works for Théâtre des Pantins and for the presentation of *Ubu-Roi* at the Théâtre de l'Oeuvre. Is invited with Lautrec and Vuillard to show with *La Libre Esthétique* in Brussels but does not send work in time.

1897
Participates in group show at Vollard's; shows lithographs at *La Libre Esthétique*. Illustrates Peter Nansen's *Marie* for *La Revue Blanche*.

1898

Participates in group show at Vollard's; represented in exhibition of French Art (van Gogh, Gauguin, Bonnard, Vuillard) in Oslo, Stockholm, Göteborg. Models marionettes for Franc-Nohain's *Vive la France* prohibited by censor. *Marie* appears in book form. Mellerio publishes *La lithographie originale en couleurs.*

1899

Participates in important group exhibition at Durand-Ruel's. At about this time enters into agreement with Bernheim-Jeune. Studios: rue Lechapelais and rue Ballu. Roussel settles in l'Etang-la-ville where Bonnard and Marthe frequently visit him. Vollard publishes *Quelques Aspects de la Vie de Paris.*

1900

Participates in group exhibition at Bernheim-Jeune's. Illustrates *Parallèlement* for Vollard. Begins to live partly in Paris, partly in the country near the city, notably at Montval where he rents a small house.

1901

Exhibits a large triptych at the *Indépendants.* Does vignettes for *La Revue Blanche.* Denis exhibits at the Salon his *Hommage à Cézanne* in which Bonnard is represented.

1902

Vollard publishes *Daphnis et Chloé* with illustrations by Bonnard. Participates in group show at Bernheim-Jeune's. Exhibits a bronze table centre piece at Vollard's now in Musée d'Art Moderne, Paris. Redon draws a lithograph portrait of Bonnard.

1903

Exhibits 'Portrait of Terrasse' at the *Indépendants;* participates in first *Salon d'Automne* with 3 canvases, among them 'Après-midi bourgeois'. Participates in Viennese Secession. Studio: 65 rue de Douai.

1904

One-man show at Bernheim-Jeune's. Sends 3 paintings to the *Indépendants* and 7 to the *Salon d'Automne* (some lent by Vollard); also participates in Impressionist exhibition of *La Libre Esthétique* in Brussels. Draws illustrations for Jules Renard's *Histoires Naturelles.* Stays at Médan, Villennes and Vernouillet.

1905

Exhibits 2 paintings at the *Indépendants* and 5 at the *Salon d'Automne,* where they impress André Gide. At about this time begins to spend summers at Villennes, Vernouillet or Cotteville.

1906

Exhibits at the *Indépendants,* the *Salon d'Automne* and the *Secession* in Berlin. Probably one-man show at Bernheim-Jeune's.

1907

Participates with 10 paintings in group show at Bernheim-Jeune's; exhibits a decorative panel at the *Salon d'Automne.* Has 2 paintings in French Impressionist exhibition at Prague. 1907-08, shows at Munich *Secession.* Paris studio: 60 rue de Douai in a former convent. Between 1907 and 1911 makes short trips to Belgium, Holland, England, Italy, Spain and Tunisia.

1908

Draws illustrations for Mirbeau's *La 628-E-8.* Exhibits 4 paintings at the *Salon d'Automne,* participates in jubilee exhibition of *La Libre Esthétique.*
Sale of the Natanson collection, including 27 paintings by Vuillard and 19 by Bonnard. Bonnard's canvases average 810 francs; 6 bring more than 1000 francs. Among the buyers are Fénéon, Coolus, Bernheim-Jeune, Vuillard (who acquires a 'Portrait of Thadée Natanson' of whom he himself had painted several likenesses) and Mirbeau who pays the highest price of the sale, 2050 francs for a painting which, eleven years later, at the Mirbeau sale, was to bring 6000 francs.

1909

In February one-man show at Bernheim-Jeune's with 36 paintings. Exhibits at the *Indépendants* and at *La Libre Esthétique.* Paints portrait of George Besson, 60 rue de Douai. 1909-10, works in Médan. The Académie Ranson is founded; Bonnard is the only one of the Nabis who avoids teaching there.

1910

Trip to the south of France early in the year. In March one-man show at Bernheim-Jeune's with 34 paintings. Exhibits 1 painting at the *Indépendants* and 4 decorative panels for Misia Godebska at the *Salon d'Automne* (reproduced in *L'Art Décoratif*). Represented in exhibition of French Art at Leipzig *Kunstverein;* corresponding member of Berlin *Secession.* Paris studios: 60 rue de Douai and 21 quai Voltaire.

1911
May-June, one-man show of work done in 1910-11 at Bernheim-Jeune's, including 27 paintings, a series of drawings and 'Mediterranean', 3 decorative panels executed for Morosoff, Moscow. These 3 panels are shown again at the *Salon d'Automne*.

1912
Rents a house at Saint-Germain-en-Laye. Buys *Ma Roulotte*, a small house at Vernonnet near Vernon. From then on until about 1938 divides his time between the Seine Valley and the south (Grasse, St. Tropez, Le Cannet). Exhibits at Paris Triennale, at *La Libre Esthétique* and at the *Salon d'Automne*, for the catalogue-cover of which he does a sketch. The two first long articles on Bonnard appear: a 'profile' by Thadée Natanson and a critical study by Lucie Cousturier. Together with Vuillard, Roussel and Vallotton declines Legion of Honor. Paris studio: 22 rue Tourlaque.

1913
Represented by 7 paintings in exhibition of French Art at Zurich Kunsthaus. One-man show in May-June at Bernheim-Jeune's; shows 21 recent works, catalogue illustrated with 10 pencil sketches. Contributes sketches to *Cahiers d'Aujourd'hui*. Trip with Vuillard to Holland, England and Hamburg where both painted.
Is represented by one painting in the famous Armory show in New York. Shows at *La Libre Esthétique* and at the *Salon d'Automne*. Paris studio: 22 rue Tourlaque.

1914
Represented by 5 paintings in exhibition of French 19th Century Art in Copenhagen. Sale of the Roger Marx collection, including 4 early works by Bonnard. Outbreak of First World War. From 1914-1918 Bonnard lives mostly at Saint Germain-en-Laye.

1915
Bonnard is particularly preoccupied with drawing and composition.

1916
Represented by 15 paintings in exhibition of French Art in Winterthur, Switzerland.

1917
Shows 11 paintings in exhibition of recent works at Bernheim-Jeune's in Oct.-Nov.

1918
Spends summer in Uriage. Armistice.

1919
Léon Werth publishes the first book on Bonnard. Shows 3 paintings at the *Salon d'Automne*. Paris address: 56 rue Molitor, Auteuil.

1920
Shows 1 painting at the *Indépendants*. Between 1920 and 1930 lives only infrequently in Paris. Visits Arcachon.

1921
May-June, one-man show at Bernheim-Jeune's with 24 paintings. Does not show at either *Indépendants* or *Salon d'Automne*. In 1921-22 contributes some sketches to *Cahiers d'Aujourd'hui* edited by George Besson.

1922
Represented at Venice Biennale; does not show at either *Indépendants* or *Salon d'Automne*. Bernheim-Jeune publish book on Bonnard by Coquiot. Visits Arcachon.

1923
Wins third class medal and $500 award at Carnegie International Exhibition, Pittsburgh. Shows 3 paintings at *Indépendants* and 2 at *Salon d'Automne*. Vollard prints Mirbeau's *Dingo* illustrated with etchings by Bonnard but does not release the book for another four years. Death of Claude Terrasse. Paris address: 56 rue Molitor.

1924
April, large retrospective exhibition, 1891-1922, at Galerie Druet, Paris. June-July, one-man show at Bernheim-Jeune's. Does not send anything to the *Indépendants*.

1925
Buys small house 'Le Bosquet' at Le Cannet near Cannes. Begins to do watercolours. Shows 1 painting at *Salon d'Automne*. Paris address: 48 Boulevard des Batignolles. Marries his companion of thirty years, Maria Boursin, who called herself Marthe de Moligny.

1926

Comes to U.S.A. as member of Carnegie International jury. Represented by 2 paintings at Manes Society exhibition in Prague. Has 6 paintings in retrospective at the *Indépendants*; does not show at the *Salon d'Automne*. In Nov.-Dec. one-man show of 20 recent paintings at Bernheim-Jeune's.

1927

Vollard releases *Dingo*. Shows 1 painting each at *Indépendants* and *Salon d'Automne*. The painter's nephew, Charles Terrasse, publishes a book on Bonnard.

1928

In April, de Hauke & Co. organize exhibition of 40 paintings by Bonnard in New York; catalogue introduction by Claude Anet. Shows 1 painting at *Salon d'Automne*. Paris address: 48 Boulevard des Batignolles.

1929

Represented in exhibition of Modern French Art. April-May, Palais des Beaux-Arts, Brussels. Does not show at *Indépendants*. May 16, sale of the collection of Alexandre Natanson, including some of Bonnard's sketches for *La Revue Blanche*.

1930

Represented by 7 paintings in Jan.-Feb. exhibition of 'Painting in Paris' at Museum of Modern Art, New York. Vollard publishes *La Vie de Sainte Monique*, illustrated by Bonnard. Does not show at *Indépendants*.

1931

Between 1930 and 1932 visits Arcachon.

1932

July exhibition of colour lithographs by Bonnard and drawings by Sickert at Leicester Gallery, London. Between 1932 and 1938 repeatedly visits Deauville and Trouville. Exhibition at Kunsthaus, Zurich.

1933

One-man show at Bernheim-Jeune's in June.

1934

March, exhibition of 44 paintings at Wildenstein Gallery, New York.

1935

Feb.-March, represented in exhibition *Artistes de Paris* at Palais des Beaux-Arts, Brussels. May, Bonnard exhibition at Reid and Lefevre Gallery, London. June, exhibition of Portraits by Bonnard at Galerie Braun & Co., Paris. Institute of Art, Boston: *La Vie Française*, exhibition of paintings chiefly by Bonnard and Vuillard.

1936

Wins second prize at Carnegie International Exhibition. Represented in exhibition of *Peintres de la Revue Blanche*, organized by Bolette Natanson in Paris. December, represented by 19 paintings in exhibition of works by Bonnard and Vuillard, Galerie Paul Rosenberg, Paris.

1937

June-October, represented with large group of works at Paris World's Fair, *Les Maîtres de l'Art Indépendant*. 6 paintings in group show at Tooth & Sons, London, May-June.

1938

March-April, represented in group shows at Rosenberg & Helft Gallery, London, and at Durand-Ruel's, Paris, in May-June. December 1938-January 1939, loan exhibition of paintings and prints by Bonnard and Vuillard at Art Institute of Chicago.

1939

February-April, represented at exhibition *Parijsche Schilders* at Municipal Museum, Amsterdam. March, 51 paintings in retrospective at Svensk-Franska Konstgalleriet, Stockholm. Exhibition of works by Bonnard, Laprade, Bouche at Durand-Ruel's in Paris. June, exhibition of 40 pastels, watercolours and drawings by Bonnard and van Dongen at J. Rodrigues-Henriques. Does not show at the *Indépendants*. Upon outbreak of Second World War, Bonnard remains in Le Cannet: does not return to Paris before 1945.

1940

Defeat of France. Death of Madame Bonnard and of Vuillard. To avoid complications, Bonnard fakes a will of his wife; while this went undetected during his lifetime, it has to lead to grave legal complications concerning the artist's estate.

1941

Sale of part of the Fénéon Collection in Paris: 6 paintings by Bonnard bring close to one million francs. 12 paintings exhibited at Galerie Petridès, Paris.

1942

March, show of Bonnard drawings, watercolours and prints at Weyhe Gallery, New York.

1943

Represented by 4 paintings in Bonnard-Vuillard exhibition, Paul Rosenberg and Co., New York.

1944

Illustrates a group of early letters for Tériade, editor of *Verve*, published in facsimile under title: *Correspondances*. *Formes et Couleurs* (Switzerland) and *Le Point* publish special issues devoted to Bonnard. Graphic work exhibited at Pierre Bérès Gallery, Paris.
Liberation of France.

1945

Short visit to Paris. Nov.-Dec., exhibition of 40 gouaches, pastels, watercolours and drawings by Bonnard and Marquet at J. Rodrigues-Henriques'. Bonnard writes short introduction for exhibition of work by Stephane Agasse at same gallery.

1946

June-July, retrospective show of 34 major works organized by Bernheim-Jeune's, rue Desbordes-Valmore, Paris. Dec. 1946-Jan. 1947, exhibition of 15 paintings at Bignou Gallery, New York. Bonnard agrees to project of large retrospective show to be organized by Museum of Modern Art, New York, to celebrate his eightieth birthday in 1947. Prepares with Tériade a special *Verve* issue which he arranges and illustrates. Shows at the *Salon d'Automne*.

1947

January 23, death of Bonnard in Le Cannet.
Feb., exhibition of 13 paintings at Galerie Georges Moos, Zurich. Feb.-March, represented by 2 decorative panels in exhibition *Sur 4 Murs*, Galerie Maeght, Paris. March, the *Indépendants* organize 'Hommage à Pierre Bonnard', including 11 paintings. The artist's nephew arranges retrospective exhibitions in Copenhagen, Amsterdam (77 paintings, drawings, etc.). June-July, represented by 16 paintings in exhibition 'Bonnard and his French Contemporaries', Lefevre Gallery, London. Sept., exhibition of 34 paintings and 20 lithographs at Svensk-Franska Konstgalleriet, Stockholm. Oct.-Dec., large retrospective exhibition at Paris Orangerie (*c.* 100 paintings, 27 drawings, watercolours and gouaches, 33 prints, 17 illustrated books).

261   **Mi-Carême** *c.* 1893

Ne fronce plus ces sourcils-ci,
Casta, ni cette bouche-ci,
Laisse-moi puiser tous tes baumes,
Piana, sucrés, salés, poivrés,
Et laisse-moi boire, poivrés,
Salés, sucrés, tes sacrés baumes.

351   **A page from Parallèlement** 1900

List of Abbreviations

Amsterdam, 1947.	Amsterdam, Stedelijk Museum. Exhibition, *Bonnard*, 1947.
Basle, 1955.	Basle, Kunsthalle. Exhibition, *Bonnard*, 1955.
Beer.	F. J. Beer, *Bonnard*, 1947.
Besson.	Georges Besson, *Bonnard*, 1934.
Brunswick, Bremen, Cologne, 1956-7.	Exhibition, *Bonnard*, 1956-7.
Buenos Aires, 1965.	Wildenstein, Buenos Aires. Exhibition, *Bonnard*, 1965.
Copenhagen, 1947.	Copenhagen, Ny Carlsberg Glyptotek. Exhibition, *Bonnard*, 1947.
Coquiot.	Gustave Coquiot, *Bonnard*, 1922.
Courthion.	Pierre Courthion, *Bonnard, Peintre du Merveilleux*, 1945.
Edinburgh, 1948.	Edinburgh, Royal Scottish Academy. Arts Council Exhibition, *Bonnard and Vuillard*, 1948.
Fosca.	François Fosca, *Bonnard*, 1919.
Lyon, 1954.	Lyon, Musée des Beaux-Arts. Exhibition, *Bonnard*, 1954.
Milan, 1955.	Milan, Palazzo della Permanente. Exhibition, *Bonnard*, 1955.
Natanson.	Thadée Natanson, *Le Bonnard que je propose*, 1951.
New York, 1948.	New York, Museum of Modern Art, and Cleveland Museum of Art. Exhibition, *Bonnard*, 1948.
New York, 1964-5.	New York, Museum of Modern Art, Los Angeles, County Museum, and Chicago. Exhibition, *Bonnard and his Environment*, 1964-5.
Nice, 1955.	Nice, Musée des Ponchettes. Exhibition, *Bonnard*, 1955.
Orangerie, 1947.	Paris, Musée de l'Orangerie. Exhibition, *Bonnard*, 1947.
Paris, 1955.	Paris, Musée d'Art Moderne. Exhibition, *Bonnard, Vuillard et les Nabis, 1888-1903*, 1955.
Paris, Druet, 1924	Paris, Galerie Druet. Exhibition, *Bonnard 1891 à 1922*, 1924.
Rewald.	John Rewald, *Bonnard*, 1948.
Roger-Marx.	C. Roger-Marx, *Bonnard, Lithographe*, 1952.

Rotterdam, 1953.	Rotterdam, Boymans Museum. Exhibition, *Bonnard*, 1953.
R.A.	Royal Academy.
Rumpel.	H. Rumpel, *Bonnard*, 1952.
Sutton.	Denys Sutton, *Bonnard*, 1957.
C. Terrasse.	Charles Terrasse, *Bonnard*, 1927.
A. Terrasse.	Antoine Terrasse, *Bonnard*, 1964.
Vaillant	Annette Vaillant, *Bonnard*, 1965.
Werth.	Léon Werth, *Bonnard*, 1923.
Zurich, 1949.	Zurich, Kunsthaus. Exhibition, *Bonnard*, 1949.

300   **Nude** *c.* 1938-40

Catalogue

Oil paintings

In the descriptions height precedes width.

The abbreviations used under 'Exh.' and 'Lit.' are amplified in the lists given on preceding pages.

As the arrangement of this Exhibition could not be completed until shortly before the opening it has been impossible to follow the Academy's usual practice of numbering the catalogue entries according to the sequence of the exhibits. The order is chronological, with the drawings, lithographs and books following the paintings.

The numbers under the illustrations refer to the entries in the text of the catalogue.

1
Bouquet de Fleurs *c*. 1888

Canvas 16 × 12¼ in./40·6 × 31·1 cm.
Signed.

Lent by the Bowers Collection, Paris

2 *Illustrated p. 77*
House with a Tower (Near le Grand-Lemps)
c. 1888

Canvas 7¼ × 9 in./18·4 × 22·9 cm.

Lit.
A. Terrasse, p. 12, repr.

Le Grand-Lemps, near Côte Saint-André in Isère was the home of Bonnard's family.

Lent by a Private Collector, Paris

3
Le Jabot Rose *c*. 1890

Panel 13½ × 8 in./ 34·3 × 20·3 cm.
Signed.

Coll.
Ambroise Vollard.

Exh.
Arthur Tooth, London, *Recent Acquisitions*, 1963.

Lent by H. F. Oppenheimer, Esq.

4
La Grand-Mère aux Poules 1891

Canvas 15½ × 13½ in./39·3 × 34·3 cm.
Signed.

Coll.
Jean Terrasse.

Exh.
Musée des Beaux-Arts, Nancy, *De Daumier à Rouault*, 1963 (2).

Lit.
C. Terrasse, p. 23, repr.

While in Paris, Bonnard lived in his grandmother's house in the Rue de Parme; however, this picture was presumably painted in the country.

Lent by Monsieur Claude Terrasse

5
Boules de Neige 1891

Canvas 16 × 12¾ in./40·6 × 32·4 cm.
Signed.

Coll.
Bernheim-Jeune, Paris; Raphäel Gerard, Paris;
Knoedler, New York;
Mrs. Edward Hutton, Long Island.

Lent by the Hon. Peter Samuel

6
Deux Chiens 1891

Canvas 13½ × 14⅝ in./34·3 × 37·2 cm.
Signed and dated.

Coll.
O. Bateman Brown; Arthur Jeffress, by whom
bequeathed to the Gallery.

Lit.
K. R. Towndrow, 'Bonnard', *Apollo*, March 1952, p. 79,
repr.

Lent by Southampton Art Gallery

7 (a) *Illustrated p. 79*
Femmes au Jardin: Four Panels for a Screen
1891

Canvases each 63 × 18⅞ in./160 × 48 cm. (a) Femme
à la Robe à Pois blancs; (b) Femme assise au Chat;
(c) Femme à la Robe Quadrille; (d) Femme à la Pèlerine.
Signed.

Exh.
Salon des Indépendants, Paris, 1891 (125-128).

Lit.
Vaillant, 1965, pp. 28-29, repr. For a reproduction of
(a), see C. Terrasse, 'Recollections of Bonnard', *Apollo*,
p. 65.

Sketches for (a) and (b) were exhibited at Acquavella,
New York, 1965. Nos. 28, 29.

Two other sets of four panels (*c.* 1891-2 and *c.* 1892-5)
designed for screens are in the collection of M. Louis
Carré, Paris, and a New York private collector (see
Rewald, pp. 64-5, repr.).

Lent by Mrs. Frank Jay Gould, U.S.A.

8
Militaire et Blonde 1892

Canvas 10⅞ × 7½ in./27·5 × 19 cm.
Signed.

This subject recalls the military picture (see Rewald,
p. 61, repr.) executed by Bonnard during or after his
military service, 1889-90.

Lent by Mr. and Mrs. Charles Zadok

9
Marguerite 1892

Panel 12⅛ × 6½ in./30·9 × 16·5 cm.
Signed and dated.

Lit.
Coquiot, pl. I; C. Terrasse, 'Recollections of Bonnard',
Apollo, January, 1966, p. 65, repr.

For a chalk drawing, which is presumably a study for
this picture, see Terrasse, p. 57, repr. Another drawing
connected with this picture occurs in an unpublished
sketchbook by the artist now in a New York
private collection.

Lent by a Private Collector, U.S.A.

10 *Illustrated p. 77*
La Partie de Croquet 1892

Canvas 50⅜ × 63 in./128 × 160 cm.
Signed and dated.

Exh.
Salon des Indépendants, Paris, 1892;
Orangerie, 1947 (5); New York, 1964-5 (2).

Lit.
Coquiot, pl. II; *Bonnard; Formes et Couleurs*,
VI (11), 1944, p. 16, repr.;
A. Terrasse, p. 22, repr.

Lent by a Private Collection, U.S.A.

11
La Baignade 1893

Panel 13¾ × 10½ in./35 × 26·6 cm.
Signed and dated.

Coll.
R. A. Peto.

Exh.
Arts Council, *French Paintings from Mr. Peto's Collection*,
1951 (3);
Plymouth, *French Impressionists from the Peto Collection*,
1960 (3).

Lent by Mrs. Rosemary Peto

12 *Illustrated p. 78*
Vue Panoramique 1894

Panel 31½ × 57½ in./80 × 146 cm.
Signed and dated.

Lent by a Private Collection, U.S.A.

13
Mother and Child 1894

Panel 14½ × 17⅝ in./36·9 × 44·8 cm.
Signed and dated.

Exh.
Arts Council, 1948 (3);
Leeds, *Acquisitions of the Leeds Arts Collections Fund,
1913-49*, 1949 (2); Basle, 1955 (5); Milan, 1955 (5);
Russell-Cotes Gallery, Bournemouth, *19th Century
French Pictures*, 1960 (2).

Lent by the City Art Gallery, Leeds

14 *Illustrated p. 81*
La Rue en Hiver 1894

Panel 10¾ × 14 in./27·3 × 35·5 cm.
Signed and dated.

Coll.
Thadée Natanson, until 1908; Félix Fénéon, 1908-41;
Baronne Blanc, 1941-62.

Exh.
Munich, Secession Gallery, 1907-8 (7); Paris,
Galerie Druet, 1924 (5); Brussels, Palais des Beaux-
Arts, *L'Art Français Moderne*, 1929 (427, as 'Dans la
Rue'); Galerie E. de Frenne, Paris, *Bonnard et
Modigliani*, 1935 (1).

Lent by Mr. and Mrs. Emery Reves

15 *Illustrated p. 81*
Figures dans la Rue *c.* 1894

Board 11¼ × 15 in./28·6 × 38·1 cm.
Signed.

Exh.
Rotterdam, 1953 (6).

This may be compared with *La Rue en Hiver* (No. 14) of
1894.

Lent by Lord Sainsbury

16
A Boy eating Cherries 1895

Board 21 × 16¾ in./53·5 × 41·9 cm.
Signed and dated.

Coll.
Miss May Guinness, Dublin.

Exh.
National College of Art, Dublin, *Modern Continental
Paintings*, 1944.

Lent by a Private Collector, Ireland

17
Le Joueur d'Organe 1895

Board 16 × 10½ in./40·7 × 26·7 cm.
Signed and dated.

Coll.
Roger-Marx, Paris, 1914; Mrs. Hugh Neame, 1935.

Exh.
Arthur Tooth, London, *Recent Acquisitions IX*, 1954 (25)
and *Anthology*, 1959 (24).

No. 21 may be compared with the *Street in Eragny* in
the collection of Mrs. Mellon Bruce, New York (see
Rewald, p. 66, repr.).

Lent by Mrs. Dudley Tooth

18 *Illustrated p. 78*
Les Trois Poupées 1895

Canvas 15⅜ × 22½ in./39 × 57 cm.
Signed.

It is perhaps relevant to note that in 1897 Bonnard
modelled puppets for the Théâtre des Pantins.

Lent by a Private Collection, U.S.A.

19
Boulevard des Batignolles 1895

Board 13½ × 10 in./34·3 × 25·4 cm.
Signed.

Inscribed: *à Ronai Bonnard 95*

Coll.
Rippl-Ronai; Lefevre Gallery, London.

Exh.
Lefevre Gallery, London, *XIX and XX Century
French Paintings*, 1958 (1); Tate Gallery, *Private Views*,
1963 (74).

Josef Rippl-Ronai (1861-1927) to whom the picture is
dedicated, was born in Hungary and was certainly in
Paris by 1887 when he worked under his fellow
countryman Munkacsy. He became friends with
Bonnard, Vuillard and Maillol. He returned to Hungary
in 1902 and published his memoirs in 1911. His
portrait of Maillol, done at Banyuls in 1899, is in the
Musée d'Art Moderne, Paris.

Lent by Sir Antony and Lady Hornby

20
Races at Longchamps 1895

Panel 12¾ × 17½ in./32·5 × 44·5 cm.
Signed.

Coll.
Bernheim-Jeune, Paris.

Exh.
Brunswick, Bremen, Cologne, 1956-7 (4);
Bührle Collection at Zurich, 1958 (258); at Berlin,
1958 (60); at Munich, 1958 (1); and at Edinburgh,
1961 (65).

The subject is derived from the pictures of racecourses
painted by Degas and Manet. Bonnard also painted a
triptych of *The Course at Longchamps* in 1897 (see Beer,
pl. 23).

Lent by Mrs. Charlotte Bührle

21 *Illustrated p. 79*
Nu: Fond Verdure *c.* 1895

Canvas 55⅛ × 23⅝ in./140 × 60 cm.
Signed.

Lent by a Private Collector, New York

22
La Cueillette de Pommes *c.* 1895-96

Canvas 65½ × 40¼ in./166·3 × 102·2 cm.

Coll.
Thadée Natanson

Exh.
Galerie Charpentier, Paris, *Jardins de France*, 1943
(311) as 'Jardin de Provence'.

According to Monsieur Charles Terrasse this represents
the grand jardin de clos au Grand Lemps.

Lent by M. Knoedler and Co. Inc.

23 *Illustrated p. 82*
La Lampe *c.* 1895-96

Panel 22 × 28⅜ in./55·9 × 72·1 cm.
Signed.

Coll.
A. J. Macdonnell.

Lit.
The Studio, April 1958, p. 119, repr.; Vaillant, p. 187,
repr.

Lent by John Lowe, Esq.

24
Scène de Rue *c.* 1895-96

Panel 10⅝ × 6¾ in./27 × 17 cm.
Studio stamp.

Lent by the Bowers Collection, Paris

25
Roof Tops *c.* 1895-1900

Panel 13½ × 14½ in./34·3 × 36·8 cm.
Inscribed: *Bonnard à Paul Ganis*.

Coll.
Paul Ganis; Mrs. Adele R. Levy, Chicago.

Exh.
New York 1948 (6a); 1964-5 (7).

Lit.
Rewald, p. 67, repr.

This picture may be compared with Bonnard's *Maison
dans la Cour*, published in the series of 12 lithographs in
1899 (cf. Roger-Marx, No. 59).

Lent by Smith College Museum of Art, Northampton, Mass.

26 *Illustrated p. 80*
Les Grands Boulevards *c.* 1895-1900

Canvas 10⅝ × 13¼ in./27 × 33·6 cm.
Signed.

Coll.
Wildenstein, 1937.

Exh.
Roland, Browse and Delbanco, London, *Bonnard*,
1950 (21); Rotterdam, 1953 (17); Milan, 1955 (9);
Basle, 1955 (10); Nice, 1955 (5); Musée de L'Art
Moderne, Paris, *Les Sources du XXme Siècle*, 1960-1 (40).

The picture may be compared with the *Sortie de L'Ecole*
of *c.* 1893, in the Lauder Greenway Collection, New
York (see Beer, pl. 28).

Lent by Mr. and Mrs. R. J. Sainsbury

27
Le Quatorze Juillet *c.* 1896

Canvas laid on panel 22¾ × 26¾ in./58 × 68 cm.
Signed.

Exh.
Galerie Giroux, Brussels, *Art Français*, 1947 (2); Liège,
Ghent and Luxembourg, *Bonnard, Vuillard, Denis*,
1948; Ghent, *La Peinture dans les Collections Gantoises*,
1953 (24); Paris, 1955 (71); Brussels, Palais de France,
International Exhibition, 1958; Paris, Musée National
d'Art Moderne, *L'école de Paris dans les Collections Belges*,
1959 (8).

No. 27 may be compared with the *At the Moulin Rouge*
of 1896 in the Wright Ludington Collection, Santa
Barbara (see Rewald, p. 69, repr.).

Lent by the Collection Leten, Ghent

28 *Illustrated p. 78*
Canotage sur la Seine *c.* 1897

Panel 12½ × 23½ in./31·7 × 59·7 cm.
Signed.

Coll.
Joseph Hessel, Paris; Kapferer, Paris.

Exh.
New York, 1964-5 (8); Buenos Aires, 1965 (13).

Lit.
Vaillant, p. 35, repr.

Bonnard made a lithograph of this subject (*Le Canotage*)
in 1897 in the second *Album des Peintres Graveurs*: cf.
Roger Marx, No. 44.

Lent by a Private Collection, New York

29
Paris: Night Scene *c.* 1897-1900

Paper on canvas 19½ × 22 in./49·5 × 55·9 cm.
Studio Stamp.

Lent by the Bowers Collection, Paris

30
Les Persiennes 1897

Board 16¼ × 8¾ in./42 × 22 cm.
Signed.

Coll.
Denys Cochin.

Exh.
Rotterdam, 1953 (9); Basle, 1955 (7); Milan, 1955 (16).

Lent by J. O'Hana, Esq.

31
Nu couché, Bras levés *c.* 1898

Panel 15¾ × 22¾ in./40 × 58 cm.
Signed.

Coll.
Félix Fénéon.

Exh.
Paris, Druet, 1924; New York, 1948 (10).

Lent by Monsieur H. Decoin

32 *Illustrated p. 80*
La Place Clichy 1898

Panel 23¼ × 30¼ in./59 × 77 cm.
Signed and dated.

Coll.
Ambroise Vollard.

Exh.
Marlborough Gallery, London, *Roussel, Bonnard,
Vuillard*, 1954 (35).

Lent by Charles Clore, Esq.

33
Intérieur avec petits Garçons 1898

Board 21¼ × 13¾ in./54 × 35 cm.

Exh.
Arthur Tooth, London, *Recent Acquisitions*, 1965 (16).

Lit.
Natanson, Fig. 17.

A related picture is in the Collection of Mr. Norton
Simon.

Lent by Leonard Wolfson, Esq.

34 *Illustrated p. 80*
Chez la Brodeuse *c.* 1898

Panel 13½ × 16 in./34·3 × 40·6 cm.
Signed.

Coll.
Mme Eugène Zak; Mme Jeanne Castel;
Arthur Jeffress; the Hon. Mrs. A. Pleydell-Bouverie

Exh.
Rotterdam, 1953 (5, as *c.* 1895).

Lit.
Beer, pl. 41.

Lent by Cecil G. Bernstein, Esq.

35
La Foire *c.* 1898

Panel 13¾ × 10⅝ in./35 × 27 cm.

Exh.
New York, 1948 (9); Kunsthalle, Berne, *Maler der Revue Blanche*, 1951 (223); Bellier, Paris, *Bonnard*, 1960 (2).

Lit.
Rewald, 1948, p. 25, repr.

Lent by Maître A. Bellier

36 *Illustrated p. 80*
La Lampe à l'Huile 1898-1900

Board 24 × 22¾ in./60·9 × 57·8 cm.

Coll.
Paul Pétrides Gallery, Paris.

Exh.
Arthur Tooth, London, *Recent Acquisitions*, 1953 (17); Tate Gallery, London, *Private Views*, 1963 (119).

Lit.
Sutton, pl. 2.

Lent by Mrs. Oliver Parker

37 *Illustrated p. 82*
Le Repas 1899

Panel 12⅝ × 16 in./32·1 × 40·6 cm.
Signed and dated.

Coll.
Joseph Hessel; Lefevre Gallery, London.

Exh.
Lefevre Gallery, London, *Bonnard and his French Contemporaries*, 1947 (8); Arts Council, *French Paintings from Mr. Peto's Collection*, 1947 (2); Edinburgh, 1948 (9); Rotterdam, 1953 (14); Marlborough Gallery, London, *Roussel, Bonnard, Vuillard*, 1954 (36); Plymouth, *French Impressionists from the Peto Collection*, 1960 (4).

Lit.
Tristan Bernard, 'Joseph Hessel', *La Renaissance* (n.d.) p. 36, repr.

Lent by Mrs. Rosemary Peto

38
Le Jardin: La Famille Terrasse 1899

Board 13 × 20 in./33 × 50·8 cm.
Signed and dated.

Coll.
Henri Bernstein.

Exh.
Lefevre Gallery, London, *XIX and XX Century French Paintings*, 1962 (1).

Lent by a Private Collector

39 *Illustrated p. 80*
Interior: The Terrasse Children 1899

Panel 12½ × 21 in./31·6 × 53·3 cm.
Signed and dated.

Coll.
Georges Renand.

Exh.
Rotterdam, 1953 (16).

Lit.
F. Jourdain, *Bonnard ou les Vertus de la Liberté*, 1946, repr.

Lent by Mr. and Mrs. Emery Reves

40
L'Indolente: Femme assoupie sur un Lit 1899

Canvas 37¾ × 41⅜ in./96 × 105 cm.
Signed and dated.

Coll.
Alexandre Natanson; Félix Fénéon.

Exh.
Orangerie, 1947 (15: as *L'Assoupie*); Liège, Ghent and Luxembourg, *Bonnard, Vuillard, Denis*, 1948; Brussels, Amsterdam, *Cent Chefs-d'oeuvre du Musée d'Art Moderne*, 1952 (2).

Lit.
Sutton, pl. 3.
B. Dorival, *L'Ecole de Paris au Musée d'Art Moderne*, 1961, pp. 100-101.

Lent by the Musée National d'Art Moderne, Paris

41 *Illustrated p. 80*
L'Indolente: Femme assoupie sur un Lit *c.* 1899

Canvas 35 × 41½ in./88·9 × 105·4 cm.
Studio stamp.

This is another version of No. 40.

Lent by the Bowers Collection, Paris

42 *Illustrated p. 83*
La Marchande de Quatre Saisons *c.* 1899

Canvas 21⅝ × 24⅜ in./55 × 62 cm.

A lithograph of the same title is included in the series, *Quelques Aspects de la Vie de Paris*, 1895 (cf. Roger-Marx, No. 63).

Lit.
Vaillant, p. 43, repr.

Lent by a Private Collection, U.S.A.

43
La Place Pigalle 1900

Panel 13 × 23 in./33 × 58·4 cm.
Signed.

Coll.
Galerie Georges Petit, Paris 1930; Bernheim-Jeune, Paris; de Frenne, Paris, 1948; French Art Galleries, Inc., New York; Mr. and Mrs. Max Miller, New York; Lefevre Gallery, London.

Exh.
Galerie Charpentier, Paris, *Scènes et Figures Parisiennes*, 1943 (487 as 'La Rue'); New York, 1948 (13); Lefevre Gallery, London, *XIX and XX Century French Paintings*, 1963 (1).

Lit.
Paul Fierens, *Emporium*, 1935, p. 81; Beer, pl. 31; Natanson, pl. 26 (as 'Montmartre').

Lent by Sir Isaac Wolfson, Bt.

44
Misia Godebska 1900

Canvas 25 × 20 in./61 × 50 cm.
Signed.

Coll.
André Weil; O'Hana Gallery, London.

Exh.
Milan, 1955 (31, as 1912).

Lit.
Sutton, pl. 4.

Misia Godebska (**1872-1950**) was born in St. Petersburg, her father being a Polish painter and her mother of Belgian and Russian extraction. She studied music under Fauré and when little over fifteen married Thadée Natanson, the nephew of her father's second wife. Her salon in the rue Saint-Florentin and her house at Valvins were visited by many of the leading artists and men of letters of the day. After being divorced by Natanson, she married Alfred Edwards, the founder of the Paris daily paper *Le Matin*, and later J. M. Sert, the Spanish painter. Her portrait was painted by Renoir, Toulouse-Lautrec, Bonnard, Vuillard, and Valloton. She commissioned Bonnard to paint a series of decorations for her drawing room, one of which is included in the exhibition (No. 91).

Lent by Mrs. Maurice Harris

45 *Illustrated p. 83*
Paris: Night 1900

Board 17¾ × 22½ in./45 × 57 cm.
Signed and dated.

Coll.
Galerie Druet, Paris, 1924; Fayet; J. T. Spaulding, 1938-48.

Exh.
Fogg Museum, Cambridge, Mass., *Paris in Paintings*, 1941; Rhode Island School of Design, Providence, 1951; Society of the Four Arts, Palm Beach, Florida, *Bonnard*, 1957; Minneapolis Institute of Arts, *The Nabis and their Circle* 1962 (unnumbered).

Lit.
J. Rewald, 'For Pierre Bonnard on his seventy-fifth birthday', *Art News*, XLI, 1942, p. 24.

Lent by the Museum of Fine Arts, Boston (Bequest of J. T. Spaulding)

46 *Illustrated p. 86*

La Famille Terrasse, ou l'Après-Midi Bourgeoise
1900

Canvas 54¾ × 83½ in./139 × 212 cm.
Signed.

Exh.
First at the Salon des Indépendants, Paris, 1900, and on
numerous subsequent occasions, including Orangerie,
1947 (20); New York, 1948 (17); Rotterdam, 1953
(25); Lyon, 1954 (15); Nice, 1955 (6); Bernheim-Jeune,
Paris, *Hommage à Bonnard*, 1956 (4), and *Cent Ans de
Portrait*, 1962 (3); Stockholm, *La douce France*, 1964 (55).

Lit.
The main references, from an extensive bibliography
are C. Terrasse, pp. 97-8, repr. p. 99; Rewald, pp. 37,
repr. 38; Natanson, pp. 216-35.

The scene takes place at the Grand-Lemps, Isère, the
house of Mme Eugène Bonnard, mother of the artist
and of Mme Claude Terrasse. On the bench at the left
is Claude Terrasse and his son Jean; seated in the
centre beside Mme Terrasse, Mme Prudhomme with
her godson, Charles Terrasse, and at the extreme right
M. Prudhomme. Mme Bonnard is disappearing
through the french window. Three other Terrasse
children are portrayed: Vivette, in the foreground with
her nurse, Robert seated by the pool and Renée in the
window. Another version is in the Stuttgart Gallery.

Lent by The Collection Bernheim-Jeune, Paris

47
Le Linge 1900

Board 20 × 12½ in./50·8 × 31·8 cm.
Signed and dated.

Coll.
Joseph Hessel, Paris.

Exh.
Arts Council, *French Paintings from Mr. Peto's Collection*,
1947 (3); Edinburgh, 1948 (11); Marlborough Gallery,
London, *Roussel, Bonnard, Vuillard*, 1954 (37).

Lit.
Tristan Bernard, 'Joseph Hessel', *La Renaissance* (n.d.),
p. 32.

Lent by Mrs. Rosemary Peto

48
Scène de Rue *c.* 1900

Paper on canvas 18⅞ × 21⅝ in./48 × 55 cm.
Studio Stamp.

Lent by the Bowers Collection, Paris

49 *Illustrated p. 84*
Thadée Natanson et jeune Femme *c.* 1900-3

Panel 31¾ × 21¼ in./81 × 54 cm.
Studio Stamp.

Thadée Natanson (1868-1951) was born in Poland and
came to Paris with his family as a child. He became
friends with Lucien Herr, Charles Andler, and Léon
Blum. He was a lawyer, but his interests led him into
artistic and literary circles and he became editor-in-
chief of *La Revue Blanche* of which his brother
Alexandre was the director. He played an active part
in the Dreyfus affair and he was one of the founders of
the *Ligue des Droits de l'Homme*. He was painted by
Bonnard, Vuillard and Josef Rippl-Ronai. His wife,
Misia, also sat to numerous artists, among them
Bonnard. (See No. 56).

Lent by the Bowers Collection, Paris

50
Snow Scene *c.* 1900-5

Canvas 15 × 33½ in./38 × 85 cm.
Studio Stamp.

Lent by the Bowers Collection, Paris

51
Deux Femmes *c.* 1901-7

Panel 14⅝ × 18⅛ in./37 × 46 cm.
Studio Stamp.

Lent by the Bowers Collection, Paris

52
Les Enfants Terrasse *c.* 1902

Canvas 19¼ × 21¼ in./49 × 54 cm.

Coll.
Bernheim-Jeune, Paris; Dr. Emil Hahnloser, Zurich.

Exh.
Zurich, *Bonnard-Vuillard*, 1932 (19); Zurich, 1949 (19);
Kunsthalle, Berne, *Maler der Revue Blanche*, 1951 (14).

Lit.
Vaillant, p. 49, repr.

Lent by a Private Collector, Switzerland

53
Dans le Port *c.* 1902-3

Canvas 19 × 21½ in./48 × 54½ cm.
Signed.

Coll.
Edouard Vuillard; Jacques Roussel.

Exh.
Buenos Aires, 1965 (4); Santa Barbara, *Painters by the Sea*, 1961; Dallas, *ibid.*; Dallas, *Collector's Choice*, 1961.

This work appears in a picture by Vuillard, *Mme Vuillard at the Table* in the Parnis-Livingstone Collection: cf. Vuillard Exhibition Catalogue, Wildenstein, New York, 1964 (61).

Lent by the Gallery Maeght, Paris

54
Leçons 1903

Canvas 14½ × 18 in./36·8 × 45·7 cm.
Signed.

Coll.
Mayor Gallery, London; Angus Wilson; Odo Cross.

Exh.
Roland, Browse and Delbanco, London, *Bonnard*, 1950 (32); Southampton Art Gallery, 1951-61.

Lit.
C. Terrasse, p. 87 (as *La Dinette*, 1903).

Lent by the Barber Institute of Fine Arts, University of Birmingham

55
Interior with two Children 1903

Board 20½ × 15⅜ in./52 × 39 cm.
Signed.

Coll.
Katia Granoff, Paris, 1948.

Exh.
Zurich, 1949 (18); Lyon, 1954 (20); Basle, 1955 (17); Milan, 1955 (13).

Lent by Dr. Ing. Willi Aebi

56
Misia Godebska on a Boat *c.* 1903

Canvas 21¾ × 18¼ in./55·2 × 46·3 cm.
Signed.

Coll.
Lefevre Gallery, London; Knoedler, New York.

Exh.
Lefevre Gallery, London, *French Painters of Today*, 1924 (1).

Lent by a Private Collector, Paris

57
Nude 1903

Board 26¾ × 20½ in./68 × 52 cm.
Signed.

Coll.
Consul General Jean Jahnson, Stockholm; Svensk-Franska Konstgalleriet, Stockholm, 1934.

Exh.
Liljevalchs Konsthall, Stockholm, *Cézanne till Picasso*, 1954 (14); Milan, 1955 (19).

Lit.
Werth, pl. 2 (as 1903).

Lent by the Konstmuseum, Gothenburg

58
Nude *c.* 1903

Board 20½ × 17½ in./52 × 44·3 cm.
Signed.

Coll.
Gösta Olsson; Svensk-Franska Konstgalleriet, Stockholm, 1918.

Exh.
Liljevalchs Konsthall, Stockholm, *Cézanne till Picasso*, 1954 (16); Milan, 1955 (20).

Lent by the Konstmuseum, Gothenburg

59 *Illustrated p. 92*
Interior with Woman seated 1905

Canvas 19 × 17 in./48·2 × 43·2 cm.
Signed.

Coll.
Roger Fry, by whom presented to the Institute, 1935.

Exh.
Lyon, 1954 (22).

Lent by the Courtauld Institute Galleries (Fry Collection)

60 *Illustrated p. 84*
Le Ruban rose *c.* 1905

Canvas 21½ × 24⅞ in./54·6 × 63 cm.
Signed.

Exh.
Orangerie, 1947 (hors catalogue); Nice, 1955 (7).

Lent by Dr. Jacques Dupont

61
Woman seated in a Studio *c.* 1905

Canvas 24½ × 19 in./62·2 × 48·3 cm.
Signed.

Coll.
Edward G. Robinson.

Exh.
Los Angeles, *The Edward G. Robinson Collection*, 1941;
New York, *Forty Paintings from Edward G. Robinson
Collection*, 1953 (2); Tate Gallery, London, *Niarchos
Collection*, 1958 (as 1909); Zurich, 1959 (28).

Lent by Stavros S. Niarchos, Esq.

62 *Illustrated p. 84*
Femme aux Bas noirs *c.* 1905

Board 24½ × 25¼ in./62·2 × 64·1 cm.
Signed.

Exh.
Kunsthalle, Berne, *Maler der Revue Blanche*, 1951
(13); Rotterdam, 1953 (42); Basle, 1955 (21); Petit
Palais, Paris, *De Géricault à Matisse*, 1959 (3).

Lit.
Fosca, pl. XXV; C. Terrasse, pl. 101;
F. Jourdain, *Bonnard, ou les Vertus de la Liberté*, 1946,
repr.; Natanson, pl. 39 (as 1909); Rumpel, pl. 22.

Lent by the Galerie Rosengart, Lucerne

63
Scène de Rue *c.* 1905-10

Board 61¾ × 68⅛ in./157 × 173 cm.
Studio Stamp.

Lent by the Bowers Collection, Paris

64
Le Goûter 1906

Canvas 25½ × 36¾ in./65 × 92 cm.
Signed.

Exh.
New York, 1948; Bellier, Paris, *Bonnard*, 1960 (8).

Lent by Mme Bellier

65 *Illustrated p. 85*
Repas de Bêtes *c.* 1906

Canvas 42½ × 29½ in./108 × 74·9 cm.
Signed.

Coll.
Joseph Hessel, Paris; Stern, Stockholm.

Exh.
The Hague, 1936; Marlborough Gallery, London,
French Masters of the XIX and XX Century, 1950 (2);
New York, 1964-5 (16).

The sitters are Mme Terrasse and Claude Terrasse,
the brother of Charles Terrasse.

Lent by Hugo L. Moser, Esq.

66 *Illustrated p. 85*
Sur le Yacht 1906

Panel 14½ × 18⅛ in./37 × 46 cm.
Signed.

Coll.
André Brisson, by whom presented to the Museum,
1953.

Exh.
Lyon, 1954 (25); Milan, 1955 (17); Basle, 1955 (24);
Brunswick, Bremen, Cologne 1956-7 (9).

Lit.
M. Sandoz, *Musée de Poitiers, Petites Monographies,
Collection Brisson*, n.d., p. 8, repr. 19, No. 14.

Lent by the Musée des Beaux-Arts de Poitiers

67
Shipping on the Seine *c.* 1906

Board 13 × 21 in./34 × 54 cm.
Signed.

Coll.
Purchased from the artist in 1906.

Exh.
Rotterdam, 1953 (38).

Lent by a Private Collector

68
Femme au Chien, Contre Jour *c.* 1906

Canvas 25 × 26 in./64 × 66 cm.
Studio Stamp.

This represents Marthe Bonnard with her dog 'Black'.

Lent by a Private Collector, New York

69
Torse de Femme *c.* 1906-7

Canvas 25⅝ × 24¼ in./65 × 54 cm.
Studio Stamp.

Lent by a Private Collector, New York

70
Les Demoiselles Natanson *c.* 1906-10

Canvas 48¾ × 55 in./123·9 × 39·7 cm.
Signed.

Coll.
Alexandre Natanson.

Exh.
Amsterdam, 1947 (5); Zurich, 1949 (32); Rotterdam,
1953 (42); Lyon, 1954 (14); Basle, 1955 (32);
Milan, 1955 (16); Buenos Aires, 1965 (17).

Lit.
André Fontainas, *Bonnard*, 1928, pl. X; L. Hautecoeur,
Litterature et Peinture en France, 1942, pl. XXX, VIII;
Natanson, Fig. 41 (as 1900); Vaillant, p. 61 repr.

The sitters are the daughters of Alexandre Natanson;
Evelyn, Bolette, Georgette and Marcelle.

Lent by a Private Collector, Paris

71 *Illustrated p. 93*
Dans le Cabinet de Toilette 1907

Board 42⅛ × 28⅜ in./107 × 72 cm.
Signed and dated.

Exh.
On a number of occasions, including Orangerie, 1947
(45); Rotterdam, 1953 (39); Lyon, 1954 (28); Milan,
1955 (23); Nice, 1955 (10); Basle, 1955 (27); Bernheim-
Jeune, Paris, *Hommage à Bonnard*, 1956 (11) and
Visages et Paysages de Bonnard et de Vuillard, 1957 (10);
Amsterdam, 1957 (7).

Lit.
Werth, pl. 17; Beer, p. 17, repr.

Lent by the Collection Bernheim-Jeune, Paris

72
La Femme au Chien *c.* 1907

Canvas 16 × 19 in./40·6 × 48·2 cm.

Exh.
Paris, Druet, 1924.

Lent by A. Morhange, Esq.

73
Snow Scene, Paris *c.* 1907

Canvas 12⅞ × 17⅜ in./32·7 × 44·2 cm.

Coll.
Paul Rosenberg, New York.

Exh.
New York, 1948 (23).

Lit.
Werth, No. 12, repr.

Lent by Lazarus Phillips, Esq.

74 *Illustrated p. 86*
Le Clocher 1907

Canvas 19¾ × 28¾ in./50·2 × 73 cm.
Signed.

Coll.
Bernheim-Jeune, Paris; Marquis de Ganay, Paris;
Templeton Crocker, San Francisco.

Exh.
Palace of Legion of Honour, San Francisco, 1940;
Arthur Tooth, London, *Paris-Londres*, 1962 (20).

Lent by D. F. Hellings, Esq.

75
Pêcheurs en Barque, Mer de Bretagne *c.* 1907

Canvas 26 × 30 in./66 × 76·2 cm.
Signed.

Coll.
Bernheim-Jeune, Paris.

Exh.
Rotterdam, 1953 (68, as *c.* 1924); Milan, 1955 (54, as *c.*
1925); Basle, 1955 (71); Volkswagenwerk, Wolfsberg,
Französische Malerei, 1961 (2).

Lent by the Collection S. Rosengart, Lucerne

76
Nude *c.* 1907

Canvas 21 × 13½ in./53·3 × 34·3 cm.
Signed.

Coll.
F. Hindley Smith, by whom bequeathed to the
Museum, 1939.

Lit.
Ashmolean Museum, *Catalogue of Paintings*, 1962,
p. 25, No. 58 (as *c.* 1920).

Lent by the Ashmolean Museum, Oxford

77
Misia on a Divan *c.* 1907

Canvas 32 × 46 in./80 × 115 cm.

Coll.
Misia Sert, Paris; Boulos Ristelheuber; Knoedler,
New York.

Exh.
Orangerie, 1947 (27); Dayton Art Institute, Ohio,
Chrysler Collection, 1960 (87).

Lit.
Besson, pl. 31.

For another portrait of Misia Sert see No. 44.

Lent by the Collection of Walter P. Chrysler, Jr.

78
Coin de Maison *c.* 1907-10

Canvas 29⅛ × 15 in./74 × 38 cm.
Studio Stamp.

Lent by a Private Collection, U.S.A.

79
Woman in an Interior *c.* 1907-10

Canvas 18¾ × 17¾ in./47·6 × 45·1 cm.
Signed.

Coll.
Bernheim-Jeune, Paris; Redfern Gallery, 1937.

Exh.
Paris, Druet, 1924; Redfern Gallery, 1937; National
Gallery, Cape Town, 1959 (5).

Lent by Fairfax Hall, Esq.

80 *Illustrated p. 87*
Le Paon ou les Trois Grâces 1908

Canvas 42½ × 49¼ in./108 × 125 cm.
Signed.

Exh.
First at Bernheim-Jeune, Paris, *Oeuvres Récentes*, 1909
(4); among later exhibitions, Orangerie, 1947 (43);
Bernheim-Jeune, Paris, *Hommage à Bonnard*, 1956 (19)
and *Visages et Paysages de Bonnard et de Vuillard*, 1957 (1).

Lit.
The main references are C. Terrasse, p. 124, repr. (as
'vers 1912'); Besson, pl. 29; Natanson, p. 41.

Lent by the Collection Bernheim-Jeune, Paris

81 *Illustrated p. 87*
Fin de Repas au Jardin 1908

Canvas 42⅛ × 48½ in./107 × 123 cm.
Signed and dated.

Exh.
Salon d'Automne, Paris, 1908 (187); Bernheim-Jeune,
Paris, *Hommage à Bonnard*, 1956 (16) and *Visages et
Paysages de Bonnard et de Vuillard*, 1957 (5).

Lit.
L. Cousturier, 'Bonnard', *L'Art Décoratif*, XIV, 1912,
p. 361, repr., 367; Coquiot, p. 47, repr.

Lent by the Collection Bernheim-Jeune, Paris

82
La Loge 1908

Canvas 35⅞ × 47¼ in./91 × 120 cm.
Signed.

Exh.
On a number of occasions, including New York, 1948
(24); Rotterdam, 1953 (40); Lyon, 1954 (30); Nice,
1955 (11); Bernheim-Jeune, Paris, *Hommage à Bonnard*,
1956 (13) and *Visages et Paysages de Bonnard et de
Vuillard*, 1957 (8); Musée d'Art Moderne, Paris,
Sources du XXme Siècle, 1960 (43); Stockholm, *La douce
France*, 1964 (56).

Lit.
The main references are Rewald, p. 75, repr.; Natanson,
No. 34, repr.; Besson, pl. 21.
Gaston and Josse Bernheim-Jeune with their wives.

Lent by the Collection Bernheim-Jeune, Paris

83
Nu à Contre-Jour, 1908-9

Canvas 49¼ × 42⅞ in./125 × 109 cm.
Signed.

Coll.
Octave Maus; Mlle Eugénie Hauman.

Exh.
On a number of occasions, including Brussels, *La
Libre Esthetique*, 1909 (10, as *L'Eau de Cologne*);
Orangerie, 1947 (28); Lyon, 1954 (31); Milan, 1955
(24); Basle, 1955 (30); Paris, Musée d'Art Moderne,
Les Sources du XXe Siècle, 1960 (45).

Lit.
Various Belgian periodicals in 1909; Natanson, p. 35
repr.; A. Terrasse, p. 103, repr.; Vaillant, p. 192 repr.

*Lent by the Musées Royaux des Beaux-Arts
de Belgique, Brussels*

84
Dans le Jardin *c*. 1908

Canvas 15⅛ × 18¼ in./38·4 × 46·3 cm.
Studio Stamp.

Lent by Dr. Fritz and Dr. Peter Nathan

85
La Famille Terrasse *c*. 1908

Canvas 25½ × 32½ in./64·8 × 82·5 cm.
Signed.

Coll.
Sir Alexander Korda; Mrs. A. Metcalfe.

Exh.
Arthur Tooth, London, *Paris-Londres*, 1954 (15).

This may be compared with the *Children in a Garden* of
1908 and the *Terrasse Family* of *c*. 1904: both exh. New
York, 1964-5, Nos. 15 (repr. p. 70) and 18 (repr. p. 37).

Lent by Miriam, Lady Marks

86
Nude seated on the Edge of a Bed: Bas Noir *c*. 1908

Panel 22¾ × 17 in./58·8 × 43·2 cm.

Coll.
Aristide Maillol; Lefevre Gallery, London.

Exh.
Lefevre Gallery, London, *XIX and XX Century French
Paintings*, 1956 (1); Los Angeles, 1965 (4).

Lent by The Earl of Rosslyn

87 *Illustrated p. 92*
Young Girl reading *c*.1908

Canvas 20½ × 19½ in./52·1 × 49·5 cm.
Signed.

Coll.
Terrasse.

Lent by Monsieur J.-C.Eger

88
Les deux Fauteuils *c*. 1908

Canvas 17¾ × 21¾ in./45 × 55·3 cm.
Signed.

Coll.
Bernheim-Jeune, Paris; Réaubourg, Paris; Wildenstein,
New York.

Exh.
Marlborough Gallery, London, *A Great Period of French
Painting*, 1963 (2, as *c*. 1929).

Lit.
The Connoisseur, June 1960, repr. on cover.

Lent by Terence Kennedy, Esq.

89 *Illustrated p. 88*
Siesta – The Artist's Studio *c*. 1908-10

Canvas 43 × 51½ in./109·2 × 130·9 cm.
Signed.

Coll.
Ambroise Vollard, Paris; Bernheim-Jeune, Paris;
Sir Kenneth Clark; Mrs. S. Kaye, London; Lefevre
Gallery, London.

Exh.
Lefevre Gallery, London, *Bonnard and his French
Contemporaries*, 1947 (10); New York, 1948 (26).

Lit.
C. Terrasse, p. 79, repr.; A. Fontainas, *Bonnard*, 1928,
pl. 3 (as 'La Sieste'); Beer, pl. 61 (as 'La Sieste');
Rewald, p. 80, repr.

*Lent by The National Gallery of Victoria, Melbourne
(Felton Bequest)*

90 *Illustrated p. 93*
Nude *c*. 1909

Canvas 54½ × 31½ in./138·4 × 80 cm.
Signed.

Coll.
Bernheim-Jeune, Paris; E. J. Power, London.

Lent by Art Properties Inc., New York

91 *Illustrated p. 90*
Après le Déluge 1909-10

Canvas 168⅛ × 98¼ in./425 × 249 cm.
Signed.

Coll.
Misia Sert, Paris; Private Collection, France, 1954;
Galerie Charpentier, 1954.

Exh.
Salon d'Automne, 1910; Museum of Modern Art,
New York, 1955; Portland Art Museum, Oregon,
Paintings from Private Collections, 1956-7.

Lit.
L. Cousturier, *L'Art Décoratif*, October 1910, XII,
pp. 144-7, repr.; *idem*, *L'Art Décoratif*, December 1912,
pp. 361-76, repr.; *Life Magazine*, December 1955, p. 28,
repr.; *Paintings from the Collection of Walter P. Chrysler, Jr.*
1956 (92); Roseline Bacou, 'Décors d'Appartements au
Temps des Nabis', *Art de France*, 1964, pp. 196, 202-203,
repr.

One of the group of four decorative pictures
commissioned by Misia Godebska in 1909, after her
separation from Thadée Natanson. Two are in the
collection of Mme Henri Kapferer, one of which was
exhibited at the Palais Galleria, Paris, *Paris 09-22*, 1957
(25). Writing about this decoration, Cousturier
declared: 'Rien de plus moderne, et rien de plus
filialement attaché à la tradition'.

Lent by the Collection of Walter P. Chrysler, Jr.

92 *Illustrated p. 90*
The Blue Balcony 1909-10

Canvas 20¾ × 30¼ in./52·7 × 76·5 cm.
Signed.

Coll.
Bernheim-Jeune, Paris, 1909-10;
Hugo Nathan, Munich; Paul Vallotton, Lausanne,
1915; Percy Moore Turner; Samuel Courtauld, by
whom presented to the Institute, 1932.

Exh.
Zurich, 1949 (52).

Lit.
D. Cooper, *The Courtauld Collection*, 1954, p. 83 (2),
pl. 64; *The Courtauld Institute Galleries: Catalogue*, 1965,
p. 11 (38).

Lent by the Courtauld Institute Galleries (Courtauld Collection)

93
Marine 1910

Canvas 9⅞ × 15 in./25 × 38 cm.
Signed.

Exh.
Studio Opera d'Arte, Rome, *Bonnard, Vuillard, Roussel*,
1964 (unnumbered).

Lent by a Private Collector, Germany

94
La Neige en Dauphiné *c.* 1910

Canvas 22 × 25⅛ in./55·8 × 64 cm.
Signed.

Exh.
Nice, 1955 (14); Bernheim-Jeune, Paris, *Hommage à
Bonnard*, 1956 (18); Secession Gallery, Munich,
Europäische Kunst, 1964 (41).

Lit.
A. Terrasse, p. 51, repr.

Lent by a Private Collector, Paris

95
L'Effet de Neige près de Chambéry *c.* 1910

Board 15 × 16 in./38·1 × 40·6 cm.
Signed.

Coll.
Knoedler, *c.* 1930.

Exh.
Edinburgh, 1948 (50); Roland, Browse and
Delbanco, London, *Bonnard*, 1950 (22).

Lent by a Private Collector

96
Coquelicots au Pot de Grès *c.* 1910

Canvas 28 × 21¼ in./71 × 54 cm.

Coll.
Bernheim-Jeune, Paris; Sacha Guitry, Paris, 1911;
Marlborough Fine Art.

Exh.
Galerie de Paris, *Importants Tableaux Modernes*, 1961-2
(2); Marlborough Gallery, London, *French Paintings
from English Private Collections*, 1965 (1).

Lent by a Private Collection

97
Interior: Lamplight *c.* 1910-15

Canvas 25⅝ × 19 ⁹⁄₁₆ in./65 × 49 cm.

Coll.
Carlo Grassi, Milan.

Exh.
Milan, 1955 (30a).

Lit.
G. Nicodemi *La Raccolta Carlo Grassi*, 1957, p. 167, fig. 117.

Lent by the Galleria Civica d'Arte, Moderna, Milan

98 *Illustrated p. 89*
Paysage à trois Personnages et Saule 1911

Canvas 28⅜ × 26¾ in./72 × 68 cm.
Studio Stamp.

Exh.
Rome Studio Opera d'Arte, *Bonnard, Vuillard, Roussel*, 1964 (unnumbered).

A sketch for the right-hand side of the decorative scheme which was commissioned by the Russian collector Morosoff for his Moscow house and which is now distributed between the Pushkin Museum, Moscow and The Hermitage, Leningrad. These pictures were exhibited at Bernheim-Jeune and at the Salon d'Automne in 1911 under the title of *La Médit erranée*.

Lent by the Galerie Maeght, Paris

99 *Illustrated p. 86*
Boulevard de Clichy *c.* 1911

Canvas 19½ × 27 in./49·5 × 68·5 cm.
Signed.

Coll.
Redfern Gallery, *c.* 1938.

Exh.
National College of Art, Dublin, *Modern Continental Paintings*, 1944.

This may be compared with the *Morning in Paris* and *Evening in Paris*, both of 1911, formerly in the Morosoff Collection and now in The Hermitage, Leningrad (Leningrad Cat. nos. 9107, 9105, repr.; P. Descargues, *The Hermitage*, 1961, pp. 228-229).

Lent by The Municipal Gallery of Modern Art, Dublin

100
Nature Morte avec Figure *c.* 1912

Canvas 15½ × 27¾ in./39·4 × 70·5 cm.
Signed.

Coll.
Bernheim-Jeune, Paris, 1912.

Exh.
Zurich, *Bonnard-Vuillard*, 1932 (36); Lucerne, *Sammberg Hahnloser*, 1940 (15); Milan, 1955 (29).

Lit.
L. Cousturier, *L'Art Décoratif*, 1920, p. 374; Coquiot, p. 52; Vaillant, p. 174, repr.

The woman is Marthe Bonnard.

Lent by a Private Collector, Switzerland

101
Landscape 1912

Canvas 19½ × 25 in./99·5 × 63·5 cm.
Signed.

Coll.
Odo Cross; Angus Wilson; Arthur Tooth, London, 1965.

Exh.
Institute of Contemporary Art, London, *Forty Years of Modern Art*, 1948 (5); Edinburgh, 1948 (32).

Lit.
Roger-Marx, *Bonnard*, 1924, p. 35, repr. (as *Bords de la Seine*).

This picture is also known as *Paysage près de Giverny* and *Vernonnet*.

Lent by the Aberdeen Art Gallery

102 *Illustrated p. 84*
Nu accroupi dans un Tub 1912

Canvas 30 × 40 in./76·2 × 101·6 cm.
Signed and dated.

Coll.
Félix Fénéon, Paris; Henri Belien, Brussels; Knoedler, New York.

Exh.
Zurich, 1949 (49);
Marlborough Fine Art, London, *XIX and XX Century French Masters*, 1955 (2);
Musée d'Art Moderne, Paris, *L'Ecole de Paris dans les Collections Belges*, 1959 (13).

Lent by Mr. Henry Ford II

103
Le Jardin des Tuileries *c*. 1912

Canvas 19⅛ × 25⅝ in./49 × 65 cm.
Studio Stamp.

Lit.
Vaillant, p. 71, repr.

Lent by the Collection Bloch

104
Le Jardin: Cactus *c*. 1912

Canvas 27⅛ × 24¾ in./69 × 62 cm.

Lent by a Private Collector, Switzerland

105
Nature Morte au Basset *c*. 1912

Canvas 20¼ × 24½ in./51·4 × 62·3 cm.
Signed.

Coll.
Bernheim-Jeune, Paris, 1912; Joseph Hessel, Paris;
Lefevre Gallery, London; A. Daber, Paris; private
collection, Paris; Lefevre Gallery, London.

Exh.
Lefevre Gallery, London, *Entente Cordiale*, 1939 (3);
Daber Gallery, Paris, 1942; Lefevre Gallery, London,
XIX and XX Century Paintings, 1965 (2).

Lit.
Coquiot, pp. 51-2; *The Studio*, 118, 1939, p. 144;
Courthion, p. 149, repr.; Beer, p. 130, pl. 110;
No. 105 may be compared with *Après le Déjeuner* of 1905
(see Natanson, fig. 31).

Lent by Mr. and Mrs. Paul Mellon

106
Campagne Provençale *c*. 1912

Canvas 17¾ × 29⅞ in./44 × 76 cm.
Signed.

Coll.
Galerie Rosengart, Lucerne.

Exh.
Zurich, 1949 (52); Rotterdam, 1953 (47); Basle, 1955
(43); Nice, 1955 (15).

Lit.
Courthion, p. 45, repr.

Lent by Frau Irene Vogel

107
Avenue du Bois de Boulogne *c*. 1912-14

Canvas 19⅝ × 25⅝ in./50 × 65 cm.
Studio Stamp.

Lit.
Vaillant, p. 73, repr.

Lent by a Private Collection, U.S.A.

108
**Femme blonde, nue, de Dos près d'une
Cheminée** 1913

Canvas 31½ × 20⅛ in./80 × 51 cm.
Signed.

Exh.
Bernheim-Jeune, Paris: *XXXIV Peintures de Bonnard*,
1946 (15); *Bonnard*, 1950 (20); *Hommage à Bonnard*,
1956 (21).

Lit.
C. Terrasse, p. 13, repr.; Beer, pl. IX.

Lent by the Collection Bernheim-Jeune, Paris

109
Pont de la Concorde 1913

Canvas 23⅝ × 32¾ in./60 × 83 cm.
Signed.

Coll.
Bernheim-Jeune, Paris, bought from the artist, 1913;
Montague Shearman, London; Redfern Gallery,
London; Earl of Sandwich, who presented it to the
Gallery, 1944.

Exh., Lit. see *Tate Gallery Catalogue: Foreign Paintings*,
1959, No. 5462.

A view from the Pont de la Concorde looking up the
Seine towards the Ile de la Cité and Notre-Dame.

Lent by the Tate Gallery, London

110
Jeune Fille jouant avec un Chien, Vernon 1913

Canvas 29½ × 31½ in./75 × 80 cm.
Signed.

Exh.
Bernheim-Jeune, Paris: *Bonnard*, 1946 (16); *Bonnard*,
1950 (28); *Visages et Paysages de Bonnard et de Vuillard*,
1957 (10).

Lit.
Werth, pl. 26; E. Blomberg, 'Bonnard', *Konstrevy*, 1939,
p. 4, repr.; Beer, No. 8, repr.

Lent by the Collection Morgan Snell, Paris

111
Evening at the Uhlenhorsten Ferry 1913

Canvas 19⅝ × 25½ in./49·8 × 65·5 cm.
Signed.

Coll.
Bought from the artist, 1913.

Exh.
Brunswick, Bremen, Cologne, 1956-7 (17).

Lit.
A. Lichtwark, *Briefe an die Kommission für die Verwaltung der Kunsthalle*, ed. G. Pauli, 1925, vol. 2, pp. 494-5.

Bonnard and Vuillard visited Hamburg on the invitation of Alfred Lichtwark in the summer of 1913. While he was there Bonnard painted the two pictures exhibited as Nos. 111 and 112.

Lent by the Kunsthalle, Hamburg

112
Coloured Lamp Contest on the Aussenalster 1913

Canvas 14¾ × 18¾ in./37·5 × 47·5 cm.
Signed.

Coll.
Bought from the artist 1913.

Lit.
C. Terrasse, 'Recollections of Bonnard', *Apollo*, January 1966, p. 67, repr.
See No. 111.

Lent by the Kunsthalle, Hamburg

113 *Illustrated p. 88*
The Regatta *c.* 1913

Canvas 28⅝ × 39¼ in./72·7 × 99·7 cm.
Signed.

Exh.
New York, 1964-5 (19).

Lit.
Chronique des Arts, supp. to *Gazette des Beaux-Arts*, February 1964, p. 75; Vaillant, p. 55, repr.

When he was in Hamburg with Vuillard in 1913, Bonnard was taken to see the regatta.
The present picture, which represents the regatta at Hamburg, was probably painted by Bonnard on his return to Paris.

Lent by the Museum of Art, Carnegie Institute, Pittsburgh

114
Au Jardin: Conversation dans le Parc *c.* 1913

Canvas 35½ × 28 in./90 × 71 cm.
Studio Stamp.

Probably painted during the **artist's** visit to Hamburg in 1913, or soon afterwards (see **No.** 111).

Lent by Mr. and Mrs. Charles Zadok

115
Les Faunes *before* 1914

Canvas 50⅝ × 57⅝ in./128·5 × 146·4 cm.

Coll.
(?) Bernheim-Jeune, Paris, 1916.

Exh.
Orangerie, 1947 (23, as 1905).

Lit.
Vaillant, p. 179, repr. (as *Le Crépuscule*).

Bonnard painted a composition **entitled,** *Les petits Faunes* in 1910 (cf. A. Terrasse, **p. 95 repr.**).

Lent by Frau Doctor L. Jaeggli-Hahnloser

116
Lane at Vernonnet *before* 1914

Canvas 29¼ × 24¾ in./74·3 × 62·8 cm.

Coll.
Bernheim-Jeune, Paris, 1914; De Frenne, Paris, 1937; Lefevre Gallery, London, 1947; Sir Alfred Chester Beatty.

Exh.
Lefevre Gallery, London. *Bonnard and his French Contemporaries*, 1947 (12); on **loan to** National Gallery, London, *Chester Beatty Collection*, 1956-61.

Lit.
Fosca, Pl. XIX.

Painted before 1914. After the picture was bought by Bernheim-Jeune, Bonnard retouched some of the colours without changing the **design.**

Lent by the National Gallery of Scotland, Edinburgh

117
After the Shower
(La Femme au Peignoir) 1914

Canvas 37½ × 26¼ in./95·2 × 66 cm.
Signed and dated.

Coll.
Bernheim-Jeune, Paris; M. Bühler, Berne, 1926;
Galerie Rosengart, Lucerne, 1946; Louis E. Stern,
New York.

Exh.
New York, 1948 (31, as *After the Shower*); Rosenberg
Gallery, New York, *Bonnard*, 1956 (5); Museum of Art,
Brooklyn, *The Louis E. Stern Collection*, 1962-3 (1).

Lit.
Coquiot, pl. 22 (as *Après la Douche*); *L'Amour de l'Art*,
February 1926, p. 59; *Le Point: Bonnard*, 1943, p. 33 (as
Le Cabinet de Toilette); Rewald, repr. frontispiece.

*Lent by the Philadelphia Museum of Art (Louis E. Stern
Collection)*

118 *Illustrated p. 91*
Still Life 1914

Canvas 24½ × 18 in./62·3 × 45·8 cm.
Signed.

Lit.
The Studio, May 1958, p. 148.

Lent by Mrs. Nikolas Ghika

119
Woman in a red Dress *c.* 1914

Board 18½ × 15 in./47 × 38·1 cm.

Coll.
The Independant Gallery, London; Sir Michael Sadler.

Exh.
Wiesbaden, 1914; Milan, 1955 (35); Basle, 1955 (45).

Lit.
Coquiot, pl. XXIV, as *Un Buste, 1916*.

The sitter is Mme Marthe Bonnard.

Lent by Marcus Wickam-Boynton, Esq.

120
Le Café *c.* 1914

Canvas 28¾ × 41⅞ in./73 × 106·5 cm.
Signed.

Coll.
Joseph Hessel, Paris; Bernheim-Jeune, Paris;
Independant Gallery, London, 1924; Sir Michael
Sadler, who presented it to the Gallery.

Exh., Lit., see *Tate Gallery Catalogue: Foreign
Paintings*, 1959, No. 5414.

The girl on the left may be Marthe Bonnard. The
picture has often been known as *Afternoon Tea*.

Lent by the Tate Gallery, London

121 *Illustrated p. 103*
La Porte ouverte *c.* 1914-20

Canvas 44¾ × 43½ in./113·5 × 110·5 cm.

Lit.
Vaillant, p. 86, repr.

Lent by a Private Collector, Germany

122
Jardin au Vernonnet *c.* 1915

Canvas 23¼ × 20⅞ in./59 × 53 cm.

Bonnard acquired 'Ma Roulotte', a small house at
Vernonnet, near Vernon, in 1912.

Lent by a Private Collection, U.S.A.

123
La Ferme *c.* 1915

Canvas 17¾ × 22½ in./45 × 57 cm.

Exh.
Buenos Aires, 1965 (19).

Lent by a Private Collection, U.S.A.

124
Woman with a Basket of Fruit *c.* 1915-18

Canvas 27 × 15½ in./68·6 × 39·4 cm.
Signed.

Coll.
Frederic Cone; Baltimore.

Exh.
New York, 1948 (59); Virginia, Museum of Fine Arts,
The Cone Collection, 1953; New York, 1964-5 (24).

Lit.
Rewald, p. 141, No. 59 (as 1928); Lincoln F. Johnson, Jr.,
'Pierre Bonnard and Impression' *The Baltimore Museum
of Art News*, December 1953, pp. 4-6, repr.; *Handbook of
the Cone Collection*, 1955, p. 27, No. 5, repr. p. 28.

Lent by the Baltimore Museum of Art (Cone Collection)

125
The Bridge at Vernon *c.* 1915-20

Board 12 × 14½ in./30·5 × 36·8 cm.
Signed.

Coll.
M. de Lackmann; Mlle R. Monchiaté; Mme L.
Bourdon.

Exh.
Roland, Browse and Delbanco, London, *Bonnard*, 1950
(33); Southampton and Bournemouth, *Collection H.
Roland*, 1952 (2); Milan, 1955 (39); Basle 1955 (50);
Manchester, *Collection H. Roland*, 1962 (13); Leeds,
Collection H. Roland, 1965 (13).

Lent by Dr. H. M. Roland

126
Torse de Femme vu dans un Miroir 1916

Canvas 31⅞ × 43¾ in./81 × 111 cm.
Signed.

Exh.
First at Pittsburgh, 1924, and *inter alia*, Bernheim-Jeune,
Paris, *Bonnard*, 1946 (11) and *Hommage à Bonnard*, 1956
(39); Nice, 1955 (29); Stockholm, *La douce France*, 1964
(57).

Lent by the Collection Bernheim-Jeune, Paris

127
Biches sous Bois *c.* 1916

Canvas 29¼ × 40½ in./74·3 × 102·8 cm.
Signed.

Coll.
Wildenstein, London, 1943.

Exh.
Edinburgh, 1948 (45).

Lent by Lady Glenconner

128 *Illustrated p. 93*
Nu debout *c.* 1916-19

Canvas 47 × 21 in./119·3 × 53·3 cm.
Signed.

Coll.
Bernheim-Jeune, Paris, 1935.

Lit.
C. Terrasse, p. 157, repr.

This may be compared with a *Nude* of 1916 repr. by
Roger-Marx, *Bonnard*, 1924, p. 39.

Lent by R. M. Coode, Esq.

129 *Illustrated p. 95*
Symphonie Pastorale 1916-20

Canvas 51⅛ × 63 in./130 × 160 cm.
Signed.

Exh.
First at Bernheim-Jeune, Paris, 1921 (1); on subsequent
occasions at this gallery, including *Hommage à Bonnard*,
1956 (28); Nice, 1955 (21).

Lit.
The main references are C. Terrasse, pp. 146, 147, repr.
148 (as *Pastorale*); Natanson, p. 140; P. Francastel,
Histoire de la Peinture Française, II, 1955, p. 180.

Lent by the Collection Bernheim-Jeune, Paris

130
Port de Cannes ou La Voile Latine 1917

Canvas 17 × 26¾ in./43 × 68 cm.
Signed.

Exh.
First at Bernheim-Jeune, Paris, *Bonnard*, 1917; on
subsequent occasions at this gallery, including *Hommage
à Bonnard*, 1956 (25), *Visages et Paysages de Bonnard et de
Vuillard*, 1957 (2) and *Paysages de France*, 1964 (4).

Lit.
F. Fosca, 'Bonnard', *Art et Décoration*, XXXVII, 1920,
p. 74, repr.; Beer, p. 84, No. 104, repr.; 'Les Chefs-
d'oeuvre de Bonnard doivent rester en France',
Le Temps de Paris, 17th May 1956.

Lent by the Collection Bernheim-Jeune, Paris

131
Nu devant la Cheminée 1917

Canvas 24⅜ × 19⅛ in./62 × 48·5 cm.
Signed.

Coll.
Paul Vallotton; Richard Bühler; Dr. Carl Mettler.

Exh.
Amsterdam, 1947 (23); Zurich, 1949 (76);
Mulhouse, *Bonnard*, 1951 (28); Lyon, 1954 (39);
Milan, 1955 (40); Basle, 1955 (55); Nice, 1955 (18).

Lit.
Courthion, p. 113, repr.

Lent by the Kunstmuseum, Basle

132
Hommage à Maillol (Le Statue de Maillol) 1917

Canvas 48¾ × 18½ in./123·8 × 47 cm.
Signed and dated.

Coll.
Bernheim-Jeune, **Paris**; Sam Salz, New York, 1949;
Louis E. Stern, New York.

Exh.
Bernheim-Jeune, Paris, *Bonnard*, 1926; Grand Palais,
Paris, *Hommage à Bonnard*, 1947; Museum of Art,
Brooklyn, *The Louis E. Stern Collection*, 1962-3 (2).

Lit.
'Stern Collection' *Philadelphia Museum of Art Bulletin*,
LIX, 1964, p. 95, **repr. (as '***Homage to Maillol*, 1917')
The Sculpture is *Bather in Chignon* by Maillol.

*Lent by the Philadelphia Museum of Art (Louis E. Stern
Collection)*

133 *Illustrated p. 94*
L'Esterel *c.* 1917

Canvas 22 × 28¾ in./56 × 73 cm.
Signed.

Coll.
Paul Vallotton.

Exh.
Amsterdam, 1947 (22); **New York**, 1948 (36); Bignon,
Paris, *La Peinture Française au Musée Municipal
d'Amsterdam*, 1950 (1); Rotterdam, 1953 (56); Boston,
1958-9 (27); Milwaukee, 1959; Columbus, Ohio,
Paintings from the Stedelijk Museum, Amsterdam, 1959;
Recklinghausen, Polatirät, Das Apollinische und das
Dionyische, 1961 (17); Louisiana, 1961; Stockholm,
1961-2.

Lit.
Bonnard, Formes et Couleurs, VI (2), 1944, p. 31, repr.;
Rewald, p. 86, repr.; Stedelijk Jubileumboeck, *Kunst
van Heden*, 1961, No. 242; Vaillant, p. 196, repr.

Lent by the Stedelijk Museum, Amsterdam

134
Nu dans la Baignoire *c.* 1917

Canvas 31½ × 17 in./80 × 43 cm.
Signed.

Coll.
Fontaine.

Exh.
New York, 1948 (35); Bellier, Paris, *Bonnard*,
1960 (13).

Lit.
Rewald, p. 84, repr.

Lent by Maître A. Bellier

135
Scène de Rue *c.* 1917-20

Canvas 15¾ × 24⅜ in./40 × 62 cm.
Studio Stamp.

Lent by the Bowers Collection, Paris

136 *Illustrated p. 93*
Fenêtre ouverte à Uriage 1918

Canvas 26¾ × 15⅜ in./68 × 39 cm.
Signed.

Coll.
G. Besson, Paris; F. Nathan, Zurich; Lefevre Gallery,
London.

Exh.
Lefevre Gallery, London, 1954 (1); Galleria d'Arte
Moderna, Turin, *La Pittura straniera nelle Collezioni
Italiane*, 1961, pl. 13.

Lit.
Besson, p. 32, repr.; R. Huyghe, *Les Contemporains*, 1949,
pl. 9; G. Marchiori, *La Pittura straniera nelle Collezioni
Italiane*, 1960.

Bonnard spent the summer of 1918 at Uriage.

Lent by Dr. Emilio Jesi

137
Fleurs des Champs 1919

Canvas 21⅝ × 19¼ in./55 × 49 cm.
Signed.

Exh.
Lefevre Gallery, London, *Bonnard*, 1935 (24);
Rotterdam, *Vier Eeuwen Stilleven*, 1954 (121); Bernheim-
Jeune, Paris, *Hommage à Bonnard*, 1956 (40), and *Fruits,
Fleurs*, etc., 1957 (1); Galerie Charpentier, Paris,
Les Jardins et les Fleurs, 1965.

Lit.
G. Hilaire, 'Féérie Intérieure', *Dimanche-Matin*, 10th
June 1956, p. 8.

Lent by the Collection Bernheim-Jeune, Paris

138 *Illustrated p. 94*
The Abduction of Europa 1919

Canvas 46¼ × 60¼ in./117·5 × 160·6 cm.
Signed.

Coll.
Bought by the Museum, 1930.

Exh.
Palace of the Legion of Honour, San Francisco,
French Paintings, 1934 (61); Carnegie Institute,
Pittsburgh, *Survey of French Painting*, 1936 (47);
New York, 1948 (37); Musée d'Art Moderne, Paris,
Masterpieces of the 20th Century, 1952 (4); Tate Gallery,
London, *Masterpieces of the XXth century*, 1952 (3);
Lyon, 1954 (42); Nelson Gallery, Kansas City,
Modern Masterpieces, 1955; Society of the Four Arts,
Palm Beach, Florida, *Bonnard*, 1957 (12);
Toledo Museum, *What is Modern Art*, 1960.

Lit.
Besson, p. 34, repr.; B.-M. Godwin, *European Paintings*,
1934, No. 234, repr. p. 235; Rewald, p. 87, repr.; *Art
News Annual*, 28, 1959, p. 100, repr.; M. Grosser, *Critical
Eye*, 1962, p. 170.

*Lent by the Toledo Museum of Art, Toledo, Ohio (Edward
Drummond Libbey Gift)*

139
The Edge of the Forest *c*. 1919

Panel 14⅝ × 18 in./37·2 × 45·7 cm.
Signed.

Coll.
Joseph Hessel, 1919; Bernheim-Jeune, 1919-20;
Dr. Soubies, 1920; Georges Bernheim; Bernheim-Jeune,
1925; Lefevre Gallery, London, 1935;
William McInnes, by whom bequeathed to the Gallery,
1944.

Exh.
Glasgow, *Spirit of France*, 1943 (58); Edinburgh, Society
of Scottish Artists, 1943 (203); National Gallery,
Edinburgh, *A Century of French Painting, 1840-1940*,
1944 (206); Glasgow, *The McInnes Collection*, 1943 (34);
Arts Council, Scotland, *McInnes Collection*, 1946 (26);
Edinburgh, 1948 (28); Arts Council, Scotland,
French Paintings of the 19th and 20th Centuries, 1959 (1);
R.A. Winter, *Primitives to Picasso*, 1962 (241).

Lit.
Le Bulletin de la Vie Artistique, June 1925, No. 23, p. 516;
Scottish Art Review, 1948, II, p. 11; Glasgow, *Catalogue of
French Paintings*, 1953, p. 56.

Lent by the Glasgow City Art Gallery and Museum

140
Siesta *c*. 1919

Canvas 39⅜ × 97½ in./100 × 243·7 cm.
Signed.

Coll.
Bernheim-Jeune, Paris; presented to the Gallery, 1931,
by the Nasjonalgalleriets Venner.

Exh.
Venice, *Biennale*, 1922 (236); Stockholm, Oslo,
Copenhagen, *Fransk genombrottskonst*, 1931 (4);
Kunstnernes Hus, Oslo, *Bonnard*, 1939 (52); Orangerie,
1947 (79).

Lit.
Kunst og kultur, 1932, p. 122, repr.; 1934, p. 151, repr.;
Nasjonalgalleriet, *Franske Maleri*, 1959, pp. 42, 43.

Lent by the Nasjonalgalleriet Oslo

141
Interior with Woman in Wicker Chair 1920

Canvas 28⅜ × 20⅛ in./72 × 51 cm.
Signed and dated.

Coll.
Presented by Föreningen för inköp av svensk och
fransk konst.

Exh.
Stockholm, Oslo, Copenhagen, *Fransk genombrottskonst*,
1931; Milan, 1955 (45); New York, 1964-5 (26).

Lit.
Konstrevy, 1929; *Nationalmuseum årsbok*, 1929, pp. 133f.

Lent by the Nationalmuseum, Stockholm

142
Red Flowers (Vase de Fleurs) 1920

Canvas 16½ × 14½ in./41·9 × 36·8 cm.
Signed and dated.

Coll.
Bernheim-Jeune, Paris, 1956; William A. Coolidge;
Knoedler, New York, 1960.

Exh.
Bernheim-Jeune, Paris, *Hommage à Bonnard*, 1956 (38).

Lent by Mr. and Mrs. Paul Mellon

143
Le Bol de Lait *c.* 1920

Canvas 44½ × 36½ in./113 × 92·7 cm.
Signed.

Coll.
Rosenberg and Helft, London, 1938.

Exh.
Rosenberg and Helft, London, *Bonnard and Vuillard*,
1938 (6); Edinburgh, 1948 (44); R.A., Diploma
Gallery, *A Painter's Collection*, 1963 (114, dated *c.* 1934).

Lit.
P. Herron, *The Changing Forms of Art*, 1955, p. 123-4;
Sutton, pl. 7.

Lent by Edward le Bas, Esq.

144
Marthe Bonnard *c.* 1920

Canvas 16¼ × 17¼ in./41·3 × 43·8 cm.

Coll.
A. Vallotton.

Lent by Lady Jamieson

145
Portrait of Vollard *c.* 1920

Canvas 37⅝ × 43½ in./95·5 × 111 cm.
Signed.

Coll.
Ambroise Vollard; entered Museum in 1950
(Succession Vollard).

Exh.
Rotterdam, *Maîtres Français du Petit Palais*, 1952-3 (1);
Asnières, *Hommage à Bonnard*, 1961 (6).

Lit.
Bonnard; Le Point, 1943, p. 15, repr.; Besson, pl. 38
(as 1900); A. Vollard, *Souvenirs d'un Marchand de
Tableaux*, 1937, p. 266.

Bonnard painted Ambroise Vollard, the well known
picture dealer, on a number of occasions, especially in
about 1904: cf. the picture in the Kunsthaus, Zurich
(Natanson, Fig. 30); he also painted him in 1934 (cf.
Chefs-d'Oeuvre des Collections Françaises, Galerie
Charpentier, Paris, 1962, p. 12, repr.).
Vollard refers to the present portrait in his *Souvenirs
d'un Marchand de Tableaux*, as follows: 'J'ai posé pour
d'autres peintres que Renoir et Cézanne, pour Bonnard
notamment, qui fit deux portraits de moi. Mais, chez
lui, je m'endormais pas, car j'avais toujours sur mes
genoux un petit chat qui était difficile à tenir'.

The paintings on the wall in this picture are by Renoir;
the sculpture is by Maillol.

Lent by the Musée du Petit-Palais, Paris

146
Bust of a Woman *c.* 1920

Canvas 17 × 26⅜ in./43 × 67 cm.
Signed.

Coll.
E. Troester, Geneva.

Exh.
Milan, 1955 (48).

Lent by Cecil Lewis, Esq.

147 *Illustrated p. 97*
Terrace at le Cannet *c.* 1920

Canvas 14⅜ × 23⅛ in./36·5 × 58·7 cm.
Signed.

Coll.
C. Maresco Pearce.

Exh.
Roland, Browse and Delbanco, *Bonnard*, 1950.

Lent by the Trustees of C. Maresco Pearce, Esq.

148
Le Cannet *c.* 1920

Canvas 23 × 16¼ in./58·4 × 41·3 cm.
Signed.

Coll.
C. Maresco Pearce.

Exh.
Roland, Browse and Delbanco, *Bonnard*, 1950.

Lent by the Trustees of C. Maresco Pearce

149
Paysage: Maison Rose au Treillage *c.* 1920

Canvas 17⅜ × 22¼ in./44 × 56·5 cm.

Lent by a Private Collector, U.S.A.

150
Intérieur *c.* 1920

Canvas 18⅞ × 24¾ in./48 × 63 cm.
Studio Stamp.

Lent by the Bowers Collection, Paris

151
**La Robe bleue: Deux Femmes et Corbeille de
Fruits** *c.* 1920

Canvas 22⅛ × 18½ in./56 × 47 cm.

Lent by a Private Collector, U.S.A.

152
Sunlight at Vernon *c.* 1920

Canvas 18½ × 21⅜ in./47 × 54·3 cm.
Signed.

Coll.
Bought from the artist by Bernheim-Jeune, 1922;
P. M. Turner; William Boyd; Redfern Gallery, London,
1943; Miss Andrews; Mrs. J. B. Priestley; Roland,
Browse and Delbanco, London, 1960; Miss M. S.
Davies, by whom bequeathed to the Museum, 1963.

Lit.
J. Ingamells, *Catalogue of Davies Bequest*, 1963, p. 24;
idem, *The Davies Collection*, 1963, No. 68; *Connoisseur*,
156, 1964, p. 117, repr.

A view of the artist's house at Vernon, Eure.

Lent by the National Museum of Wales

153
Jeune Femme au Col rose *c.* 1920

Canvas 26⅜ × 18½ in./67 × 47 cm.
Studio Stamp.

Lent by a Private Collector, New York

154 *Illustrated p. 98*
Levrette et Nature Morte *c.* 1920-25

Canvas 27⅜ × 27⅜ in./69·5 × 69·5 cm.
Studio Stamp.

The picture may date from the same period as the
Nature Morte of 1926 in the R. Hauert Collection, Paris
(see New York, 1964-5, No. 12, repr.).

Lent by a Private Collection, France

155
Intérieur: La Table rouge, la Cheminée *c.* 1920-2

Canvas 21 × 17⅜ in./53·5 × 44 cm.

This may be compared with the *Salle à Manger*, *c.* 1925,
which is repr. by Natanson, Fig. 65.

Lent by a Private Collection, U.S.A.

156 *Illustrated p. 96*
Portrait of the Artist *c.* 1920-25

Canvas 11 × 17½ in./28 × 44·5 cm.
Signed.

Lit.
Bonnard; *Le Point*, XXIV, 1943, p. 38, repr. (as 'vers
1930'). Vaillant, p. 90, repr.

Lent by a Private Collection, U.S.A.

157
Nu Debout à sa Toilette *c.* 1920-30

Canvas 43½ × 36¼ in./110 × 92 cm.
Signed.

Exh.
Galerie Charpentier, Paris, *Cent Chefs-d'Oeuvre*, 1953;
Basle, 1955 (60); Milan, 1955 (61, as 1932); Bellier,
Paris, *Bonnard*, 1960 (20); Kassel, *Documenta, III*, 1963.

Lit.
Natanson, p. 80, repr. (as 1920).

Lent by Maître A. Bellier

158 *Illustrated p. 95*
Monuments 1921

Canvas 51⅛ × 63 in./130 × 160 cm.
Signed.

Exh.
Bernheim-Jeune, Paris, *Bonnard*, 1921 (3); Paris,
Musée des Arts Décoratifs, 1925; Bernheim-Jeune,
Paris, *Au Fil de l'Eau*, 1962 (4); Stockholm, *La douce
France*, 1964 (58).

Lit.
The main references are Coquiot, pl. XX (328); C.
Terrasse, pp. 141, 145, repr.; P. Francastel, *Histoire de la
Peinture Française*, II, 1955, p. 180.

Lent by the Collection Bernheim-Jeune, Paris

159
Le Boulevard des Batignolles *c.* 1922

Canvas 24¾ × 25½ in./62·8 × 64·8 cm.
Signed.

Coll.
Sir Kenneth Clark; Mrs Benita Armstrong.

Exh.
Melbourne and Adelaide, *French and British Contemporary
Art*, 1939 (8); Roland, Browse and Delbanco, London,
Bonnard, 1950 (31); Marlborough Gallery, London,
Roussel, Bonnard, Vuillard, 1954 (39); Lefevre Gallery,
London, *XIX and XX Century Paintings*, 1956 (2).

Lent by Dr. Jacques Ch. Koerfer

160
Le Port Gris *c.* 1922

Canvas 14½ × 21¼ in./37 × 54 cm.
Signed.

Exh.
Edinburgh, 1948 (29); Bellier, Paris *Bonnard*, 1960 (15);
Kassel, *Documenta, III*, 1963.

Lent by Maître A. Bellier

161
Demoiselles d'Archachon c. 1922

Canvas 13 × 10¾ in./33 × 27·2 cm.
Signed.

Lent by the Schoneman Galleries Inc., New York

162
Le Port de Saint-Tropez 1923

Canvas 22 × 16 in./55·8 × 40·6 cm.
Signed.

Coll.
Bernheim-Jeune, Paris; Galerie Raeber, Basle, c. 1941.

Exh.
Lyon, 1954 (51); Basle, 1955 (66).

Lent by Frau Herold-Meyer

163
Nature Morte au Compotier 1923

Canvas 15⅜ × 19¾ in./39 × 50 cm.
Signed.

Exh.
Bernheim-Jeune, Paris: *XXXIV Peintures de Bonnard*,
1946 (27); *Hommage à Bonnard*, 1956 (37); Stockholm,
La douce France, 1964 (59).

Lent by the Collection Bernheim-Jeune, Paris

164
Femme nue se baissante 1923

Canvas 22¼ × 20¼ in./56·5 × 51·4 cm.
Signed.

Coll.
Lefevre Gallery, London.

Lent by The Hon. Mrs. A. Pleydell-Bouverie

165
Nude c. 1923

Canvas 17¾ × 13¼ in./44 × 35 cm.
Signed.

Coll.
Lefevre Gallery, London.

Exh.
Tate Gallery, London, *The Pleydell-Bouverie Collection*,
1954 (3).

Lent by The Hon. Mrs. A. Pleydell-Bouverie

166
Nude bending forward c. 1923

Canvas 41⅜ × 33⅛ in./105 × 84·1 cm.
Studio Stamp.

Exh.
New York, 1964-5 (29).

Lent by a Private Collector, New York

167 *Illustrated p. 96*
Portrait of the Artist c. 1923

Canvas 18⅛ × 13 in./46 × 33 cm.
Studio Stamp.

Lent by the Bowers Collection, Paris

168 *Illustrated p. 96*
Marthe Bonnard c. 1923

Canvas 31⅛ × 19¾ in./79 × 50 cm.
Signed.

Exh.
Orangerie, 1947 (59, as c. 1925); New York, 1948 (30).

Lit.
Werth, Fig. 31; C. Terrasse, p. 28 (as 1908);
Beer, pl. 76; *Portraits de Pierre Bonnard*, 1933, p. 7, repr.
(as 1911).

Lent by the Bowers Collection, Paris

169
Signac and his Friends sailing 1924

Canvas 54¾ × 49 in./137·8 × 124·5 cm.
Signed.

Coll.
Joseph Hessel, Paris.

Exh.
Amsterdam, 1947 (31); Orangerie, 1947 (97);
Rotterdam, 1953 (70); Milan, 1955 (52); Basle, 1955
(72).

Lit.
Besson, pl. 40; W. Wartmann, *Bilder aus den Kunsthaus,
Zurich*, 1936, pl. 136; Rewald, p. 94, repr.; Doris
Schmid, *Moderne Malerei*, 1950, pl. IV; Rumpel, pl. 27;
Vaillant, p. 203, repr.

Lent by the Kunsthaus, Zurich

170
Grand Nu bleu 1924

Canvas 39$\frac{3}{8}$ × 29$\frac{1}{2}$ in./100 × 75 cm.
Signed.

Exh.
First at Bernheim-Jeune, Paris, *Bonnard*, 1924, and
inter alia Rotterdam, 1953 (77); Nice, 1955 (33);
Bernheim-Jeune, Paris, *Hommage à Bonnard*, 1956 (53).

Lit.
Bulletin de la Vie Artistique, 15th February 1925, p. 85,
repr.

Lent by the Collection Bernheim-Jeune, Paris

171
La Table garnie 1924

Canvas 15 × 22 in./32 × 55 cm.
Signed.

Coll.
Bernheim-Jeune, Paris, 1924; G. Besnard, Paris;
Georges Bernheim, Paris; Bernheim-Jeune, Paris, 1933;
Lefevre Gallery, London; Scott and Son, Montreal.

Exh.
Willistead Art Gallery, Windsor, Ontario, *French
Impressionists*, 1945; Toledo, Toronto, *The Spirit of
Modern France*, 1946-47 (61); Toronto, Montreal,
Ottawa, *Paintings by European Masters*, 1954 (78);
Volkswagenwerke, *Französische Malerei*, 1961;
Ottawa, *European Paintings in Canadian Collections*, 1962
(46); New York, 1964-5 (31).

Lit.
The Art Gallery of Toronto: Paintings and Sculpture, 1959,
p. 58.

Painted at Le Cannet.

Lent by the Art Gallery of Toronto

172
Les jeunes Femmes ou la Nappe rayée 1924

Canvas 23 × 29$\frac{1}{2}$ in./58·5 × 75 cm.
Studio Stamp.

Exh.
Besançon, *1925*, 1963; Lisbon, *Un Siècle de Peinture
Française, 1850-1950*, 1965.

Lit.
A. Terrasse, p. 62, repr.

Lent by a Private Collector, Paris

173
Landscape with Olive Trees and Chapel 1924

Canvas 19 × 24 in./48·2 × 61 cm.
Signed.

Coll.
Roger Fry, by whom presented to the Institute, 1932.

Lit.
Courtauld Institute Catalogue (The Fry Collection), 1965, p. 2,
No. 7.

Painted in 1924 at Le Cannet, apparently on the advice
of Roger Fry, who probably bought it at the time.

Lent by the Courtauld Institute Galleries (Fry Collection)

174
L'Ile d'Or *c.* 1924

Canvas 18$\frac{1}{2}$ × 22$\frac{3}{4}$ in./47 × 57·8 cm.
Signed.

Exh.
Milan, 1955 (51); Basle, 1955 (69); Rhodes Gallery,
Salisbury, Rhodesia, *Rembrandt to Picasso*, 1957 (81).

Lent by the Roland, Browse and Delbanco Gallery, London

175
The Sous Bois *c.* 1924

Canvas 33$\frac{1}{2}$ × 16$\frac{1}{4}$ in./85 × 41·2 cm.
Signed.

Coll.
F. Hindley Smith, by whom bequeathed to the
Museum in 1939.

Exh.
Edinburgh, 1948 (51); Basle, 1955 (79); Milan, 1955
(58).

Lit.
Catalogue Ashmolean Museum, 1962, No. 69.

Lent by the Ashmolean Museum, Oxford

176
La Jetée *c.* 1924-34

Canvas 17 × 22⅛ in./43 × 56·2 cm.
Signed.

Coll.
Acquired by the present owner's mother, Frau
Hahnloser, direct from the artist.

Exh.
Zurich, *Bonnard-Vuillard*, 1932 (103); Zurich, 1949
(102); Galeries Royales, Ostend, *La Peinture sous le
Signe de Mer*, 1951; Winterthur, *Collection Hahnloser*,
1937 (1).

Lit.
'La Collection Hahnloser', *Du*, 1956; Vaillant, p. 131,
repr.

Lent by Frau Doktor L. Jaeggli-Hahnloser

177 *Illustrated p. 104*
Baignoire 1925

Canvas 33⅞ × 47½ in./86 × 120·5 cm., approximately:
the painted area is not a perfect rectangle.

Coll.
Bernheim-Jeune, Paris; Lord Ivor Spencer Churchill,
by whom presented in 1930.

Exh., Lit., see *Tate Gallery Catalogue : Foreign
Paintings*, 1959, No. 4495.

The woman is probably Marthe Bonnard. This is one
of the earliest pictures on a theme which the artist
returned to on various occasions.

Lent by the Tate Gallery, London

178 *Illustrated p. 98*
La Fenêtre 1925

Canvas 43¾ × 34⅞ in./105 × 88·5 cm.
Signed.

Coll.
Bernheim-Jeune, Paris; Independant Gallery, London,
1927; Lord Ivor Spencer Churchill, by whom
presented in 1930.

Exh., Lit., see *Tate Gallery Catalogue : Foreign
Paintings*, 1959, No. 4494.

Painted at Le Cannet in an apartment occupied by the
painter in the Villa Hirondelle prior to his purchase of
the Villa de Bosquet. On the table is the novel *Marie* by
Peter Nansen for which Bonnard drew the illustrations;
it was published by *La Revue Blanche* in 1898.

Lent by the Tate Gallery, London

179
La Table 1925

Canvas 40½ × 29¼ in./103 × 74 cm.
Signed.

Coll.
Bernheim-Jeune, Paris; Independant Gallery, London;
Trustees of the Courtauld Fund.

Exh., Lit., see *Tate Gallery Catalogue : Foreign
Paintings*, 1959, No. 4134.

The sitter is probably Marthe Bonnard. A similar
drawing in coloured chalk, said to have been made in
1929, is reproduced by Natanson, pl. 77.

Lent by the Tate Gallery, London

180 *Illustrated p. 98*
Nature Morte à la Lumière du Soir *c.* 1925

Canvas 21½ × 20½ in./54·5 × 52 cm.
Signed.

Coll.
Sam Salz, New York.

Exh.
Knoedler, New York, 1957;
Museum of Fine Arts, Boston, *European Masters of
our Time*, 1957; City Art Museum, St. Louis, *French Art*,
1960.

*Lent by the Fogg Art Museum, Cambridge, Mass. (Gift of
Mr. and Mrs. Joseph Pulitzer, Jnr.)*

181
Femme assise dans un Bibliothèque *c.* 1925

Canvas 41⅛ × 35⅝ in./104·5 × 90·5 cm.

Lit.
Vaillant, p. 93, repr.

Lent by a Private Collector, Mexico

182 *Illustrated p. 108*
Bateaux blancs *c.* 1925

Canvas 13 × 17⅞ in./33 × 45·5 cm.
Signed.

Coll.
Dr. F. and Dr. P. Nathan, Zurich.

Lent by Herr Walther Scharf

183
Femme au Chien; Nature Morte aux Bananes
c. 1925

Canvas 22½ × 19½ in./57 × 49 cm.
Studio Stamp.

Lent by a Private Collection, U.S.A.

184
Nature Morte aux Bananes *c.* 1925

Canvas 19½ × 20 in./49·5 × 50·8 cm.
Signed.

Coll.
Percy Moore Turner, London.

Exh.
National Gallery, London, *19th Century French Paintings*,
1942-43 (75a); Edinburgh, 1948 (34); Rotterdam,
1953 (72); Lefevre Gallery, London, *French Masters of
the XIX and XX Century*, 1952 (2); Glasgow,
Pictures to live with, 1946 (3).

Lit.
The Studio, May 1953, p. 173, repr.

Lent by A. J. McNeill Reid, Esq.

185
Bord de Mer: Les Toits violets *c.* 1925

Canvas 20½ × 23⅝ in./52 × 60 cm.

Lent by a Private Collection, Switzerland

186 *Illustrated p. 97*
Après le Déjeuner *c.* 1925

Canvas 29½ × 46 in./75 × 116·8 cm.
Signed.

Coll.
Durand-Ruel, Paris; Sam Salz, New York.

Exh.
Antwerp, 1926 (67); Basle, 1955 (90); New York,
Metropolitan Museum, 1964-5.

Lit.
Beer, fig. 71.

Lent by Mr. David Lloyd Kreeger

187
Port de Cannet *c.* 1925-26

Canvas 17⅝ × 25 in./44·8 × 63·5 cm.
Signed.

Coll.
Private Collection, San Francisco.

Lit.
C. Terrasse, 1927, p. 12, repr. (as *Port Gris*); A.
Terrasse, p. 61; Vaillant, p. 107, repr. A drawing for
the composition is repr. in Vaillant, p. 106.

Lent by a Private Collection, London

188
Vase de Fleurs: Renoncles dans un Vase bleu
c. 1925-30

Canvas 22¼ × 19 in./56·5 × 48 cm.
Studio Stamp.

Lent by a Private Collector, U.S.A.

189
La Table de Jardin 1926

Canvas 49½ × 53¾ in./125·7 × 136·5 cm.
Signed.

Coll.
Bernheim-Jeune, Paris.

Exh.
Zurich, *Bonnard-Vuillard*, 1932; Venice, *Biennale*, 1934
(105); Bellier, Paris, *Bonnard*, 1960 (25).

Painted at Grasse.

Lent by Mr. and Mrs. Henry J. Heinz II

190
Landscape near Vernon *c.* 1926

Canvas 22½ × 28½ in./57·1 × 72·3 cm.
Signed.

Exh.
Bührle Collection, Zurich, 1958 (262);
Lucerne, 1963 (51).

Lent by Mrs. Charlotte Bührle

191
Portrait of the Artist *c.* 1926

Canvas 20⅞ × 14⅛ in./53 × 36 cm.
Studio Stamp.

Exh.
New York, 1964-5 (39).

Lent by Mr. and Mrs. Charles Zadok

192 *Illustrated p. 98*
Paysage, Vu des Toits *c.* 1926-30

Canvas 30¾ × 39½ in./78 × 100 cm.
Studio Stamp.

Lent by a Private Collector, U.S.A.

193
Luncheon *c.* 1927

Canvas 16¼ × 24½ in./41·3 × 62·2 cm.
Signed.

Coll.
Bernheim-Jeune, Paris.

Exh.
Venice, *Biennale*, 1930 (99); Art Institute, Chicago,
Bonnard and Vuillard, 1938 (38); New York 1948 (54);
Lyon, 1954 (61); Museum of Modern Art, New York,
XXVth Anniversary Exhibition, 1945; Palm Beach,
Florida, *Society of the Four Arts*, 1957.

Lit.
Alfred H. Barr, *Painting and Sculpture in the Museum of
Modern Art*, 1948, p. 38, repr.; Rewald, p. 99, repr.

Lent by the Museum of Modern Art, New York

194 *Illustrated p. 108*
Bords de Seine *c.* 1928-30

Canvas 14½ × 21½ in./37 × 54·6 cm.
Signed.

Coll.
Wildenstein.

For a painting of a comparable style, see Vaillant,
p. 117, repr.

Lent by Herr Walther Scharf

195
Toits rouges du Cannet *c.* 1928-30

Canvas 21½ × 36¾ in./54·5 × 93 cm.

There is a related drawing of this view reproduced by
Natanson (p. 76) where it is dated 1928.

Lent by a Private Collector, Germany

196
Le Port de Saint-Tropez *c.* 1928-30

Canvas 14 × 22 in./35·5 × 55·8 cm.
Signed.

Exh.
Leicester Galleries, London, *Four French Painters*, 1937;
Contemporary Pictures Gallery, Dublin, 1939;
National College of Art, Dublin, *Modern Continental
Paintings*, 1944 (8).

Lent by R. R. Figgis, Esq.

197
Remorqueur à Vernon *c.* 1929

Canvas 24⅛ × 22½ in./61·3 × 56·5 cm.
Signed.

Coll.
Terrasse.

Exh.
New York, 1964-5 (45).

Lent by Mrs. Charles W. Engelhard

198
Le Port de Cannes *c.* 1930

Canvas 28⅜ × 24 in./72 × 61 cm.
Signed.

Coll.
Bernheim-Jeune, Paris, 1936.

Exh.
Musée d'Art Moderne, Paris, *Depuis Bonnard*, 1960.

Lent by a Private Collector, Paris

199
La Table de Travail 1930

Canvas 48 × 36 in./122 × 91·4 cm.
Signed.

Coll.
Paul Rosenberg, Paris.

Exh.
Venice, 1933; Brussels, *Art Français Contemporain*,
1938 (1); New York, 1948 (53); New York, 1964-5 (40).

Lit.
Rewald, p. 50, repr. 103.

No. 199 was painted by 1926, when it was subsequently
retouched.

Lent by a Private Collector, Switzerland

200
Vue du Cannet 1930

Canvas 17¾ × 14½ in./45 × 37 cm.
Signed.

Exh.
Munich, *Von Bonnard bis Heute*, 1961 (8).

Lent by a Private Collector, Paris

201
La Rue Tholozé et le Moulin de Galette 1930

Panel 17¾ × 14½ in./45 × 37 cm.
Signed.

Exh.
Munich, *Von Bonnard bis Heute*, 1961 (7).

Lent by a Private Collector, Paris

202
Paysage Classique 1930

Canvas 23¼ × 18½ in./59 × 47 cm.
Signed.

Exh.
First at Wildenstein, New York, *Bonnard*, 1934 (22);
on a number of subsequent occasions, including Nice,
1955 (36); Bernheim-Jeune, Paris, *Hommage à Bonnard*,
1956 (48) and *Paysages de Bonnard et de Vuillard*, 1957 (7);
Rouen, *Paysages de France*, 1958; Moscow, *L'Art
Français*, 1961.

Lit.
Beer, pl. XV.

Lent by the Collection Bernheim-Jeune, Paris

203 *Illustrated p. 106*
Nature Morte 1930

Canvas 14 × 14⅜ in./35·5 × 36·5 cm.

Coll.
French private collection; Ragnar Moltzau, Oslo;
acquired by the Gallery, 1960.

Exh., Lit.
See *Katalog der Staatsgalerie, Stuttgart, Neue
Meister*, 1961, p. 21, pl. 35.

Lent by the Staatsgalerie, Stuttgart

204
La Porte Molitor *c.* 1930

Canvas 31½ × 22⅜ in./80 × 57 cm.
Signed.

Exh.
Lyon, 1954 (66).

Lent by a Private Collector, Paris

205
Le Port de Saint-Tropez *c.* 1930

Canvas 11¾ × 15 in./30 × 38 cm.

Exh.
Orangerie, 1947 (67); Edinburgh, 1948 (53).

Lent by the Musée de l'Annonciade, St. Tropez

206
Sea Piece – Coast Scene *c.* 1930

Canvas 18 × 34½ in./45·8 × 87·6 cm.
Signed.

Coll.
Sir Kenneth Clark.

Exh.
Edinburgh, 1948 (54); R.A. Diploma Gallery,
A Painter's Collection, 1963 (134).

Lent by Edward le Bas, Esq.

207
The Road to Nantes *c.* 1930

Canvas 27¼ × 25⅞ in./69·2 × 65·7 cm.
Signed.

Coll.
Bernheim-Jeune, Paris; Pierre Loeb; Valentine Gallery
New York; Leonard C. Hanna, jnr.

Exh.
New York, 1948 (60); 1964-5 (50).

Lit.
Rewald, p. 104, repr.; Cleveland Museum of Art,
In Memoriam Leonard C. Hanna, jnr., 1958, No. 1, repr.

Lent by the Cleveland Museum of Art, Ohio

208 *Illustrated p. 101*
Nu à la Baignoire *c.* 1930

Canvas 40½ × 25 in./103 × 63·5 cm.

Lent by a Private Collection, U.S.A.

209
Nu à la Table de Toilette *c.* 1930

Canvas 38½ × 21⅝ in./98 × 55 cm.

Lent by a Private Collection, Switzerland

210
Nu violet *c.* 1932

Canvas 46½ × 26 in./118·5 × 66 cm.

No. 210 may be compared with the *Nu au Contre-Jour* of
c. 1932 in the National Museum, Stockholm.

Lent by a Private Collector, Canada

211
Le Nu jaune *c.* 1932

Canvas 31 × 17¾ in./78·7 × 45 cm.

Coll.
Mlles Bowers; Wildenstein.

Lent by the Galerie Beyeler, Basle

212
Saint-Tropez *c.* 1932

Canvas 82 × 104 in./208·2 × 264·1 cm.

Lent by a Private Collector, Paris

213 *Illustrated p. 100*
Femme nue au Gant *c.* 1932-35

Canvas 50 × 34¼ in./127 × 87 cm.
Studio Stamp.

Lit.
'Couleur de Bonnard', *Verve*, V, 1947, p. 69, repr.

Lent by a Private Collection, U.S.A.

214
Nude before a Mirror 1933

Canvas 59⅞ × 40⅛ in./151·7 × 102 cm.
Signed.

Exh.
Venice, *Biennale*, 1934; Nice, 1955; Basle,
1955 (84); Milan, 1955 (60); New York, 1964-5 (55).

Lit.
Besson, p. 47, repr.; *Bonnard: Le Point*, XXIV, 1943,
p. 41, repr.

Lent by the Galleria Internazionale d'Arte Moderna, Venice

215
La Corbeille de Fruits *c.* 1933

Canvas 21⅛ × 27½ in./53·5 × 70 cm.

Lent by a Private Collection, U.S.A.

216 *Illustrated p. 110*
Le Boeuf et l'Enfant *c.* 1934-46

Canvas 36⅝ × 46⅛ in./93 × 117 cm.
Signed.

Exh.
Orangerie, 1947 (41); Copenhagen, 1947 (37);
Venice, *Biennale*, 1950 (78); Buenos-Aires, 1965 (10).

Lit.
'Couleur de Bonnard', *Verve*, V, 1947, repr., p. 44;
Vaillant, p. 151, repr.

Lent by a Private Collection, U.S.A.

217
La Femme au Bain *c.* 1933

Canvas 47¼ × 43¼ in./120 × 111 cm.
Signed.

Coll.
Dupuy Freysel, by whom bought from the artist;
Beyeler, Basle, 1960.

Lit.
Besson, pl. 50 (as 1933); Beer, pl. 94; Natanson,
pl. 49 (as 'vers 1920'); H. Perruchot, 'L'Affaire
Bonnard', *L'Oeil*, October 1956, p. 13, repr.

Lent by a Private Collector, Switzerland

218
Nu accroupi dans La Baignoire 1935

Canvas 23⅝ × 31¾ in./60 × 80·5 cm.

Lit.
'Couleur de Bonnard', *Verve*, 1947; Vaillant, p. 127,
repr.

For a drawing for this picture see Vaillant, p. 126,
repr.

Lent by a Private Collection, U.S.A.

219 *Illustrated p. 105*
Nu dans le Bain 1935

Canvas 36⅝ × 57¾ in./93 × 147 cm.
Signed.

Coll.
Bought from the artist in 1937.

Exh.
On a number of occasions, including R.A., *L'Ecole de
Paris*, 1951 (38), with previous references; Milan, 1955
(63); Japan, *Art Français*, 1961-2 (237).

Lit.
L. Rosten, 'The Story behind the Painting', *Look
Magazine*, 1962, pp. 120-1, repr.; A. Martini, *Pittura in
Europa*, 1963, p. 223, repr.; G. Schurr, 'Bonnard',
Galerie des Arts, April 1965, p. 25, repr.

Lent by the Petit Palais, Paris

220
Bord de Mer *c.* 1935

Canvas 18½ × 24⅞ in./47 × 63 cm.
Studio Stamp.

Lent by the Bowers Collection, Paris

221
Paysage du Cannet *c.* 1935

Canvas 27⅝ × 31⅛ in./70 × 78 cm.
Studio Stamp.

Lent by a Private Collection, France

222
Nature Morte *c.* 1935

Canvas 12 × 15½ in./30·5 × 39·5 cm.
Studio Stamp.

Lent by a Private Collection, Germany

223 *Illustrated p. 106*
Nature Morte *c.* 1935

Canvas 17¼ × 23⅝ in./44 × 60 cm.
Studio Stamp.

Lent by a Private Collection, U.S.A.

224 *Illustrated p. 109*
Seascape at Cannes *c.* 1935

Canvas 21 × 27 in./53·3 × 68·5 cm.
Signed.

Coll.
Bernheim-Jeune, Paris, 1937.

Exh.
Roland, Browse and Delbanco, London, *Bonnard*,
1950 (4).

Lent by a Private Collector

225
Corbeille de Fruits (Le Cannet) *c.* 1935

Canvas 15⅜ × 19⅛ in./39 × 48·5 cm.
Studio Stamp.

Lent by a Private Collection, U.S.A.

226
La Corbeille: Pêches, Poires et Raisins *c.* 1935

Canvas 23⅝ × 15¾ in./60 × 40 cm.
Signed.

Coll.
Eugène Blot, 1937.

Lent by a Private Collector, Paris

227
Nu *c.* 1935

Canvas 44⅞ × 24 in./114 × 61 cm.

Lit.
'Couleur de Bonnard', *Verve*, V, 1947, repr.

Lent by the Bowers Collection, Paris

228 *Illustrated p. 102*
Paysage vert *c.* 1935

Canvas 25⅝ × 39¾ in./65 × 101 cm.
Studio Stamp.

Lent by a Private Collector, Switzerland

229 *Illustrated p. 102*
La Prairie Fleurie *c.* 1935

Canvas 35½ × 35⅝ in./90 × 90·5 cm.
Studio Stamp.

Lent by a Private Collection, U.S.A.

230 *Illustrated p. 109*
La Baie de Saint-Tropez 1936

Canvas 18½ × 22 in./47 × 55·8 cm.
Signed.

Coll.
Sam Salz, New York.

Exh.
New York, 1948 (72).

Lit.
Rewald, p. 123, repr.

Lent by a Private Collector

231
Pleine Mer *c.* 1936

Canvas 18⅛ × 28⅜ in./46 × 72 cm.
Studio Stamp.

Lent by a Private Collection, U.S.A.

232 *Illustrated p. 109*
The Yellow Boat *c.* 1936-38

Canvas 22¾ × 29⅞ in./57·8 × 75·8 cm.

Exh.
Copenhagen, 1947 (39); New York, 1964-5 (63);
Carnegie Institute, Pittsburgh, 1965.

Lit.
'Couleur de Bonnard', *Verve*, V. 1947, repr.

Lent by Mr. and Mrs. Charles Zadok

233 *Illustrated p. 100*
Nu à la Chaise *c.* 1936-38

Canvas 50 × 33 in./127 × 83·8 cm.
Studio Stamp.

Exh.
New York, 1964-5 (64).

Lit.
C. Terrasse, 'Recollections of Bonnard', *Apollo*,
January, 1966, p. 64, repr.

Lent by Mr. and Mrs. Charles Zadok

64

234 *Illustrated p. 110*
Cheval de Cirque *c.* 1936-45

Canvas 37 × 46½ in./94 × 118 cm.
Signed.

Exh.
Orangerie, 1947 (92); Copenhagen, 1947 (36);
New York, 1948 (81).

Lit.
'Couleur de Bonnard', *Verve*, V, 1947, p. 43, repr.;
A. Terrasse, p. 93, repr.; Vaillant, p. 214, repr.

Lent by a Private Collector, Paris

235 *Illustrated p. 106*
La Cafetière *c.* 1937

Canvas 26⅜ × 23⅝ in./67 × 60 cm.
Studio Stamp.

Lent by a Private Collection, U.S.A.

236
Le Golfe de Saint-Tropez *c.* 1937-40

Canvas 16¼ × 26¾ in./41 × 68 cm.

Exh.
Nice, *Peintres à Nice et sur la Côte d'Azur*, 1960 (2);
Petit Palais, Paris, *Trois Millenaires d'Art et de Marine*,
1965 (11).

Lit.
A. Terrasse, p. 78, repr.

Lent by the Musée Toulouse-Lautrec, Albi

237 *Illustrated p. 105*
Nu dans la Baignoire *c.* 1938-41

Canvas 48 × 59½ in./122 × 151 cm.

Exh.
New York, 1964-5 (71).

Lit.
C. Terrasse, 'Recollections of Bonnard', *Apollo*,
January, 1966, p. 66, repr.

Lent by Mr. and Mrs. Charles Zadok

238 *Illustrated p. 100*
Nu à la Baignoire *c.* 1938-41

Canvas 40 × 25 in./101·6 × 63·5 cm.
Studio Stamp.

Lent by a Private Collection, U.S.A.

239 *Illustrated p. 102*
Paysage: La Maison rouge *c.* 1938-41

Canvas 21¼ × 31⅞ in./54 × 81 cm.
Studio Stamp.

Lent by Mr. and Mrs. Charles Zadok

240 *Illustrated p. 104*
La Baignoire *c.* 1938-41

Canvas 36¼ × 56¾ in./92 × 144 cm.
Studio Stamp.

Lent by a Private Collection, Germany

241 *Illustrated p. 99*
Nude in Yellow (**Le grand Nu jaune**) *c.* 1938-46

Canvas 67 × 42½ in./170·2 × 108 cm.

Exh.
New York, 1964-5 (69).

Lent by a Private Collection, U.S.A.

242 *Illustrated p. 103*
L'Atelier du Peintre au Cannet ('**Le Mimosa**')
c. 1938-46

Canvas 50 × 50 in./127 × 127 cm.

Exh.
Edinburgh, 1948 (48); New York, 1964-5 (72).

Lit.
'Couleur de Bonnard', *Verve*, V, 1947, p. 8, repr.

Lent by a Private Collector, Paris

243 *Illustrated p. 100*
Le Gant de Crin 1939

Canvas 51 × 22¾ in./129·5 × 57·8 cm.
Signed.

Exh.
Copenhagen, 1947 (41).

Lit.
Vaillant, repr. p. 128.

Lent by a Private Collection, U.S.A.

244 *Illustrated p. 103*
Avant Midi: Le Cannet *c.* 1939-45

Canvas 49⅝ × 28 in./126 × 71 cm.
Signed.

Exh.
Copenhagen, 1947 (50); New York, 1964-5 (65, as *Morning: The Open Door*, 1937).

Lit.
Beer, Fig. 120; 'Couleur de Bonnard', *Verve*, V, 1947, p. 85, repr.; Vaillant, p. 212, repr.

Lent by the Bowers Collection, Paris

245
Corbeille de Fruits *c.* 1939-45

Canvas 12¼ × 15½ in./31 × 39·3 cm.

Coll.
Jacques Lindon, 1947; Mrs. Leo Glass.

Exh.
Rosenberg, New York, *Bonnard*, 1950, and 1956 (20).

Lit.
F. Jourdain, *Bonnard, ou les Vertus de la Liberté*, 1946, repr.

Lent by a Private Collector

246
Portrait of the Artist *c.* 1940

Canvas 30 × 24 in./76·2 × 61 cm.

Exh.
New York, 1964-5 (74).

Lit.
Vaillant, p. 161, repr.; C. Terrasse, 'Recollections of Bonnard', *Apollo*, January, 1966, p. 63, repr.

Lent by Wildenstein & Co., Inc., New York

247 *Illustrated p. 107*
L'Oiseau bleu *c.* 1942-43

Canvas 50¾ × 37¾ in./129 × 96 cm.
Studio Stamp.

Lent by a Private Collection, Switzerland

248
Pêches et Raisins *c.* 1943

Canvas 18½ × 13 in./47 × 33 cm.

Exh.
New York, 1964-5 (70).

Lit.
Vaillant, p. 143, repr.

Lent by a Private Collection, U.S.A.

249 *Illustrated p. 102*
Paysage, Couchant; Le Cannet *c.* 1943

Canvas 18½ × 22⅝ in./47·5 × 57·5 cm.

Lent by a Private Collection, New York

250
Jardin du Midi *c.* 1943

Canvas 26¼ × 21⅞ in./66·5 × 55·5 cm.
Studio Stamp.

Lit.
Vaillant, p. 145, repr.

Lent by a Private Collector, Switzerland

251 *Illustrated p. 103*
Le Cannet: Paysage au Toit rouge 1944-45

Canvas 26 × 22½ in./66 × 57 cm.
Signed.

Exh.
Copenhagen, 1947 (57); New York, 1948 (78); Venice, *Biennale*, 1950 (78).

Lit.
A. Terrasse, p. 96, repr.

Lent by a Private Collector, Paris

252
Le Jardin de l'Artiste: Le Cannet *c.* 1944-46

Canvas 25¼ × 20⅞ in./64 × 53 cm.
Signed.

Exh.
New York, 1948 (29); Venice, *Biennale*, 1950 (78); Milan, 1955 (69); Basle, 1955 (52); Bernheim-Jeune, Paris, *Hommage à Bonnard*, 1956 (57); Brunswick, Bremen, Cologne, Munich, 1956-7 (43).

Lit.
L'Oeil, 21, 1956, p. 25; A. Terrasse, p. 97, repr.

Lent by a Private Collector, Paris

253
Portrait of the Artist 1945

Canvas 22 × 18 in./55·9 × 45·7 cm.
Signed.

Coll.
Acquired by the present owners from the artist.

Exh.
Nice, 1945; Galerie Maeght, Paris, 1946; Grand
Palais, Paris, *Hommage à Bonnard*, 1947; Virginia
Museum of Art, Richmond, *Impressionists and
Post-Impressionists*, 1950; Fort Worth Art Center,
Texas, 1954; Rosenberg, New York, 1956 (22);
Society of the Four Arts, Palm Beach, Florida,
Bonnard, 1957 (27); New York, 1964-5 (80).

Lit.
Beer, pl. XXIV; A. Terrasse, p. 84, repr.

Bonnard's last self-portrait, said to have been painted
in the bathroom.

Lent by Mr. and Mrs. Donald S. Stralen

254 *Illustrated p. 102*
View from the Artist's Studio, Le Cannet *c.* 1945

Canvas 37¼ × 49¼ in./94·6 × 125 cm.
Signed.

Coll.
Louis Carré, 1945-6; Sidney Janis, 1951; Mr. and Mrs.
Harvey Lynde Bradley, 1952.

Exh.
Carré, Paris, *80 Cahiers d'Art*, 1945-6; Sidney Janis
Gallery, New York, *5th Anniversary Exhibition*, 1953 (4);
Munson-Williams-Proctor Institute, Utica, New York,
1963; Memorial Art Gallery, Rochester, New York,
1963; New York, 1964-5 (81).

Lent by the Milwaukee Art Center Collection

255
Instruments de Cuisine à l'Auto-Portrait 1946-47

Canvas 20½ × 14½ in./52 × 37 cm.

Lent by Monsieur Aimé Maeght, Paris

Drawings, watercolours and gouaches

256 *Illustrated p. 13*
Sketch for the Poster, France-Champagne 1889

Pen and ink 30¾ × 23¼ in./78 × 59 cm.

Exh.
Milan, 1955 (71); Paris, 1955 (80).
This is a study for the poster commissioned in 1889 and
printed by Ancourt (cf. Roger-Marx, No. 1). For
another sketch, see L. Terrasse, p. 21, repr.

Lent by the Musée des Beaux-Arts, Rheims

257
Soldats et Squellettes: Dessin de Danse Macabre
1889

Watercolour, pen and ink 7⅝ × 11⅞ in./19·5 × 30·7
cm.

Lent by a Private Collector, U.S.A.

258
Sketch for a Poster *c.* 1889

Pastel 26¾ × 31⅞ in./67 × 81 cm.
Signed.

Inscribed: *Vue d'ensemble / s'il y a lieu / le plus beau site /
de la Normandie / à 40 km. de Paris – Bain de Mer /
et de Vapeurs / Casino Cercle / Petits Chevaux / Pays boisé /
jusqu'à la mer.*

Exh.
Brunswick, Bremen, Cologne, 1956-57 (46);
Secession Gallery, Munich, *Europäischt kunst* 1964
(47, as *c.* 1897); Cassell, *Dokumenta III*, 1964 (5).

Lit.
G. Busch, 'Ein Plakatenwurf von Pierre Bonnard in
der Kunsthalle, Bremen', *Festschrift für Edouard
Trautschold*, 1965, pp. 164-9, Pls. 106-7.

Lent by the Kunsthalle, Bremen

259 *Illustrated p. 17*
Deux Nus *c.* 1890

Pencil 11⅞ × 7½ in./30·4 × 19·2 cm.

Lent by a Private Collector, U.S.A.

260
Study for an Abecedaire *c.* 1892-94

Charcoal and pencil 7 × 7⅝ in./17·7 × 19·6 cm.
Studio stamp.

Lent by Mrs. Charles Zadok

261
Mi-Carême *c.* 1893

Charcoal 12⅝ × 9⅞ in./32·1 × 25·1 cm.
Studio stamp.

Lent by Mrs. Charles Zadok

262
Mother and Child *c.* 1893

Watercolour 10 × 5 in./25·4 × 12·7 cm.

Coll.
Galerie Charpentier, Paris.

This is connected with the lithograph, *Scène de Famille*
executed for *L'Estampe Originale* (Third issue, January-
March, 1893) : cf. Roger-Marx (1952, No. 4).

Lent by Mrs. Oliver Parker

263
The Rabbits *c.* 1893

Gouache 12½ × 9 in./31·8 × 22·9 cm.
Signed.

Exh.
Delft, Prinsenhof, *Het Aquarel*, 1952;
Rotterdam, 1955 (1); Milan, 1955 (49);
Basle, 1955 (3); Brunswick, Bremen, Cologne,
Munich, 1956-7 (45).

Lent by Mrs. Walter Feilchenfeldt

264
Couverture de l'Album 1895

Lithograph in two colours 13 × 16⅛ in./33 × 41 cm.

Lit.
Roger-Marx, No. 56; U. Johnson, *Vollard*, 1944,
pp. 57-8.

The cover for *Quelques Aspects de la Vie de Paris*. The
work, which consisted of twelve plates, was published
by Vollard in 1895. See Nos. 265-75.

Lent by the Bibliothèque Nationale, Paris

265
Avenue du Bois 1895

Lithograph in five colours 12⅛ × 18⅛ in./31 × 46 cm.

Lit.
Roger-Marx, No. 57.

From *Quelques Aspects de la Vie de Paris*. See No. 264.

Lent by the Bibliothèque Nationale, Paris

266
Coin de Rue 1895

Lithograph in four colours 10⅝ × 13¾ in./27 × 35 cm.

Lit.
Roger-Marx, No. 58.

From *Quelques Aspects de la Vie de Paris*. See No. 264.

Lent by the Bibliothèque Nationale, Paris

267
Maison dans la Cour 1895

Lithograph in four colours 13¾ × 10¼ in./35 × 26 cm.

Lit.
Roger-Marx, No. 59.

From *Quelques Aspects de la Vie de Paris*. See No. 264.

Lent by the Bibliothèque Nationale, Paris

268
Rue vue d'en haut 1895

Lithograph in four colours 14½ × 8⅝ in./37 × 22 cm.

Lit.
Roger-Marx, No. 60.

From *Quelques Aspects de la Vie de Paris*. See No. 264.

Lent by the Bibliothèque Nationale, Paris

269
Boulevard 1895

Lithograph in four colours 6¾ × 17 in./17 × 43 cm.

Lit.
Roger-Marx, No. 61.

From *Quelques Aspects de la Vie de Paris*. See No. 264.

Lent by the Bibliothèque Nationale, Paris

270
Place du Soir 1895

Lithograph in four colours 6¾ × 17 in./17 × 43 cm.

Lit.
Roger-Marx, No. 62.

From *Quelques Aspects de la Vie de Paris*. See No. 264.

Lent by the Bibliothèque Nationale, Paris

271
Marchand des Quatre-Saisons 1895

Lithograph in five colours 11⅜ × 13⅜ in./29 × 34 cm.

Lit.
Roger-Marx, No. 63.

From *Quelques Aspects de la Vie de Paris*. See No. 264.

Lent by the Bibliothèque Nationale, Paris

272
Le Pont des Arts 1895

Lithograph in four colours $10\frac{5}{8} \times 16\frac{1}{8}$ in./27×41 cm.

Lit.
Roger-Marx, No. 64.

From *Quelques Aspects de la Vie de Paris*. See No. 264.

Lent by the Bibliothèque Nationale, Paris

273
Au Théâtre 1895

Lithograph in four colours $7\frac{7}{8} \times 15\frac{3}{4}$ in./20×40 cm.

Lit.
Roger-Marx, No. 65.

From *Quelques Aspects de la Vie de Paris*. See No. 264.

Lent by the Bibliothèque Nationale, Paris

274
Rue le Soir vous la Pluie 1895

Lithograph in five colours $9 \times 13\frac{3}{4}$ in./23×35 cm.

Lit.
Roger-Marx, No. 66.

From *Quelques Aspects de la Vie de Paris*. See No. 264.

Lent by the Bibliothèque Nationale, Paris

275
Coin de Rue vue d'en haut 1895

Lithograph in four colours $8\frac{1}{4} \times 14\frac{1}{8}$ in./21×36 cm.

Lit.
Roger-Marx, No. 68.

From *Quelques Aspects de la Vie de Paris*. See No. 264.

Lent by the Bibliothèque Nationale, Paris

276 *Illustrated p. 15*
Etude de Nu sur un Lit *c.* 1899

Charcoal $9\frac{5}{8} \times 12\frac{1}{4}$ in./$24 \cdot 5 \times 31 \cdot 6$ cm.

No. 276 may be connected with *L'Indolente* (No. 41).

Lent by a Private Collection, U.S.A.

277
Scène de Rue: Enfants et Chat *c.* 1899

Charcoal $18\frac{7}{8} \times 24\frac{1}{2}$ in./$48 \cdot 2 \times 62 \cdot 3$ cm.
Studio stamp.

Lent by a Private Collection, U.S.A.

278 *Illustrated p. 13*
J'ai tout donné pour rien *c.* 1899

Charcoal $13\frac{1}{2} \times 11$ in./$34 \cdot 6 \times 27 \cdot 9$ cm.
Studio stamp.

Lent by Mrs. Charles Zadok

279
L'Education *c.* 1900

Crayon and watercolour $11\frac{1}{2} \times 7\frac{3}{8}$ in./$29 \cdot 6 \times 18 \cdot 7$ cm.
A sketch for a poster.

Lent by a Private Collector

280
Femme en Costume de Scène *c.* 1905

Pencil, pen and ink and wash
$11\frac{7}{8} \times 7\frac{5}{8}$ in./$30 \cdot 3 \times 19 \cdot 3$ cm.

Lent by a Private Collector, Paris

281
Tête de Femme *c.* 1910

Pastel $11\frac{7}{8} \times 9\frac{3}{4}$ in./$29 \cdot 8 \times 24 \cdot 7$ cm.

Lent by Mrs. Charles Zadok

282
Jeune Femme portant un Plateau *c.* 1910-11

Pen and ink $9\frac{1}{2} \times 5\frac{5}{8}$ in./$24 \times 14 \cdot 3$ cm.
Studio stamp.

Lent by Mrs. Charles Zadok

283 *Illustrated p. 17*
Sketch for a Poster for Les Ballets Russe 1914

Charcoal $9\frac{7}{8} \times 6$ in./$24 \cdot 8 \times 15 \cdot 7$ cm.
Studio stamp.

A sketch for a poster (cf. Roger-Marx, No. 75).

Lent by Mrs. Charles Zadok

284
Nus: deux Positions *c.* 1915-20

Pencil $12 \times 7\frac{5}{8}$ in./$30 \cdot 3 \times 19 \cdot 5$ cm.
Studio stamp.

Lent by a Private Collector

285
Intérieur avec une Fenêtre sur la Rue *c.* 1918

Pencil $12\frac{1}{8} \times 9\frac{1}{2}$ in./$30 \cdot 5 \times 23 \cdot 9$ cm.
Studio stamp.

Lent by a Private Collector

286 *Illustrated p. 17*
Deux Têtes de Femmes *c.* 1920

Charcoal 12⅞ × 9¾ in./32·4 × 24·7 cm.
Studio stamp.

Lent by a Private Collector

287
Les Barques sur la Seine à Vernon-Vernonnet
c. 1920

Black chalk 9½ × 12⅛ in./24 × 31 cm.
Signed.

Exh.
Rodrigues-Henriques, Paris, *Bonnard*, 1939 (36).

Lent by a Private Collector, Paris

288
Sketch for Book Illustration 1922

7 × 11 in./17·8 × 27·9 cm.

One of a set of drawings for the woodcut illustrations,
cut by Yvonne Mailler, for Claude Anet's *Notes sur
l'Amour* published by Crès, Paris, 1922.
For others in this set see Nos. 288-90.

Lent by Lazarus Phillips, Esq.

289
Sketch for Book Illustration 1922

7 × 11 in./17·8 × 27·9 cm.

Lent by Lazarus Phillips, Esq.

290
Sketch for Book Illustration 1922

7 × 11 in./17·8 × 27·9 cm.

Lent by Lazarus Phillips, Esq.

291
**Intérieur: Trois Femmes autour de la Table;
la Lampe** *c.* 1923

Pastel 9 × 11⅞ in./23 × 30·4 cm.
Studio stamp.

Lent by a Private Collector

292
Le petit Chien montant sur la Table *c.* 1925

Black chalk 7⅛ × 8¼ in./18 × 21 cm.
Signed.

Exh.
Zurich, 1949 (168); Mulhouse, 1951; Lyon, 1954 (83);
Maison de la Pensée Française, Paris, 1955.

Lent by a Private Collector, Paris

293 *Illustrated p. 21*
Paysage *c.* 1925

Pencil 8¾ × 12 in./22·3 × 30·6 cm.
Studio stamp.

Lent by a Private Collector

294
Nude in Bath Tub *c.* 1925

Pencil 4⅞ × 6⅜ in./12·5 × 16·2 cm.

Lent by a Private Collector

295
Nature Morte de Fleurs à la Fenêtre *c.* 1927

Pencil 7⅝ × 5⅛ in./19·6 × 13 cm.

Lent by Mrs. Charles Zadok

296
**Isabelle Lecomte du Nouy sur le Banc avec le
Chien de Bonnard** 1929

Black chalk 9⅞ × 13⅜ in./25 × 34 cm.
Signed.

Exh.
New York, 1948 (108); Zurich, 1949 (170); Lyon,
1954 (84); Maison de la Pensée Française, Paris, 1955.

A study for a painting.

Lent by a Private Collector, Paris

297
Boulevard des Batignolles, Paris 1930

Black chalk 4¾ × 6¼ in./12 × 16 cm.
Signed.

Exh.
Rodrigues-Henriques, Paris, *Bonnard*, 1939 (25).

Lent by a Private Collector, Paris

298
Still Life with Basket and Fruit 1930

Gouache 11 × 15 in./28 × 38·1 cm.
Signed and dated 1930.

Coll.
Marcel Guérin, Paris.

Exh.
Lausanne, *Collections Suisses*, 1964 (128).

Lent by Mrs. Walter Feilchenfeldt

299
Nuage sur la Mer *c.* 1936

Watercolour and gouache 11 × 14⅜ in./28 × 36·5 cm.
Signed.

Exh.
Orangerie, 1947 (102); New York, 1948 (85);
Bernheim-Jeune, Paris, *Hommage à Bonnard*, 1956 (56).

Lent by a Private Collector, Paris

300
Nude *c.* 1938-40

Pencil 15¼ × 11¼ in./38·8 × 28·6 cm.

Coll.
Marlborough Fine Art, London.

A similar drawing is reproduced in 'Couleur de
Bonnard', *Verve*, V, 1947.

Lent by a Private Collector

301
Mme Nana Winding 1942

Charcoal 18 × 13 in./45·7 × 33 cm.
Signed.

Coll.
Given by the artist to the sitter.

Exh.
Lefevre Gallery, London, *XIX and XX Century French
Paintings*, 1959 (1).

The sitter was a sister of Paulette Renoir, wife of
Claude Renoir.

Lent by a Private Collector

302
Mlle Antoinette Bérard 1943

Gouache 25⅝ × 18⅞ in./65 × 48 cm.
Signed.

Exh.
Copenhagen, 1947 (49); Venice, *Biennale*, 1950.

Lent by Madame Ph. Boulart

Lithographs

303
La France Champagne 1891

Lithograph 30¾ × 19⅝ in./78 × 50 cm.

Lit.
Roger-Marx, No. 1.

See No. 256 for a pen and ink sketch.

Lent by the Bibliothèque Nationale, Paris

304
Scène de Famille 1893

Lithograph in four colours 7 × 12¼ in./18 × 31 cm.

Lit.
Roger-Marx, No. 4.

Plate for *L'Estampe Originale*, III, 1893.

Lent by the Bibliothèque Nationale, Paris

305
Papa, Maman 1893

Lithograph 7⅝ × 8½ in./19·5 × 21·5 cm.

Lit.
Roger-Marx, No. 6.

From a set of nineteen illustrations for *Petites Scènes
Familières*. This, the first work to be illustrated by
Bonnard with lithographs, was published in 1893. It
contained songs by Franc-Nohain, set to music by
Claude Terrasse.

Lent by the Bibliothèque Nationale, Paris

306
Do, Do, L'enfant Do 1893

Lithograph 5¾ × 9¼ in./14·5 × 23·5 cm.

Lit.
Roger-Marx, No. 7.

From *Petites Scènes Familières*. See No. 305.

Lent by the Bibliothèque Nationale, Paris

307
Pensée Triste 1893

Lithograph $3\frac{3}{4} \times 7\frac{1}{2}$ in./$9 \cdot 5 \times 19$ cm.

Lit.
Roger-Marx, No. 8.

From *Petites Scènes Familières*. See No. 305.

Lent by the Bibliothèque Nationale, Paris

308
Départ des Amis 1893

Lithograph $4\frac{7}{8} \times 8\frac{1}{2}$ in./$12 \cdot 5 \times 21 \cdot 5$ cm.

Lit.
Roger-Marx, No. 9.

From *Petites Scènes Familières*. See No. 305.

Lent by the Bibliothèque Nationale, Paris

309
Prière 1893

Lithograph $5\frac{1}{4} \times 9\frac{1}{2}$ in./$13 \cdot 5 \times 24$ cm.

Lit.
Roger-Marx, No. 10.

From *Petites Scènes Familières*. See No. 305.

Lent by the Bibliothèque Nationale, Paris

310
Chanson du Grand-Père 1893

Lithograph $4\frac{1}{8} \times 8\frac{5}{8}$ in./$10 \cdot 5 \times 22$ cm.

Lit.
Roger-Marx, No. 11.

From *Petites Scènes Familières*. See No. 305.

Lent by the Bibliothèque Nationale, Paris

311
Le Cherrier 1893

Lithograph $5\frac{1}{4} \times 9\frac{1}{2}$ in./$13 \cdot 5 \times 24$ cm.

Lit.
Roger-Marx, No. 12.

From *Petites Scènes Familières*. See No. 305.

Lent by the Bibliothèque Nationale, Paris

312
Les Heures de la Nuit 1893

Lithograph $5\frac{1}{8} \times 9$ in./13×23 cm.

Lit.
Roger-Marx, No. 13.

From *Petites Scènes Familières*. See No. 305.

Lent by the Bibliothèque Nationale, Paris

313
Qui veut les Ecopeaux 1893

Lithograph $4\frac{1}{4} \times 8\frac{5}{8}$ in./11×22 cm.

Lit.
Roger-Marx, No. 14.

From *Petites Scènes Familières*. See No. 305.

Lent by the Bibliothèque Nationale, Paris

314
Premier Air de Fifi 1893

Lithograph $4\frac{3}{8} \times 6\frac{3}{4}$ in./11×17 cm.

Lit.
Roger-Marx, No. 15.

From *Petites Scènes Familières*. See No. 305.

Lent by the Bibliothèque Nationale, Paris

315
Promenade à Ane 1893

Lithograph $3\frac{1}{2} \times 9\frac{1}{2}$ in./9×24 cm.

Lit.
Roger-Marx, No. 16.

From *Petites Scènes Familières*. See No. 305.

Lent by the Bibliothèque Nationale, Paris

316
Rêverie 1893

Lithograph $5\frac{1}{8} \times 7\frac{1}{8}$ in./13×18 cm.

Lit.
Roger-Marx, No. 17.

From *Petites Scènes Familières*. See No. 305.

Lent by the Bibliothèque Nationale, Paris

317
Danse 1893

Lithograph $3\frac{3}{8} \times 8\frac{1}{2}$ in./$8 \cdot 5 \times 21 \cdot 5$ cm.

Lit.
Roger-Marx, No. 18.

From *Petites Scènes Familières*. See No. 305.

Lent by the Bibliothèque Nationale, Paris

318
Le Dimanche Matin à la Campagne 1893

Lithograph $5\frac{1}{2} \times 9$ in./14×23 cm.

Lit.
Roger-Marx, No. 19.

From *Petites Scènes Familières*. See No. 305.

Lent by the Bibliothèque Nationale, Paris

319
L'Angélus du Matin 1893

Lithograph $5\frac{1}{4} \times 9$ in./$13 \cdot 5 \times 23$ cm.

Lit.
Roger-Marx, No. 20.

From *Petites Scènes Familières*. See No. 305.

Lent by the Bibliothèque Nationale, Paris

320
Boutique à cinq Sous 1893

Lithograph $4\frac{7}{8} \times 8\frac{7}{8}$ in./$12 \cdot 5 \times 22 \cdot 5$ cm.

Lit.
Roger-Marx, No. 21.

From *Petites Scènes Familières*. See No. 305.

Lent by the Bibliothèque Nationale, Paris

321
La Baraque 1893

Lithograph $4\frac{1}{8} \times 8\frac{7}{8}$ in./$10 \cdot 5 \times 21 \cdot 5$ cm.

Lit.
Roger-Marx, No. 22.

From *Petites Scènes Familières*. See No. 305.

Lent by the Bibliothèque Nationale, Paris

322
Au Cirque: la Haute-Ecole 1893

Lithograph $3\frac{1}{8} \times 9\frac{1}{4}$ in./$8 \times 23 \cdot 5$ cm.

Lit.
Roger-Marx, No. 23.

From *Petites Scènes Familières*. See No. 305.

Lent by the Bibliothèque Nationale, Paris

323
Quadrille (**La Fête au Village**) 1893

Lithograph $4\frac{1}{4} \times 9\frac{1}{4}$ in./$11 \times 23 \cdot 5$ cm.

Lit.
Roger-Marx, No. 24.

From *Petites Scènes Familières*. See No. 305.

Lent by the Bibliothèque Nationale, Paris

324
Les Chiens 1893

Lithograph $10\frac{5}{8} \times 11$ in./27×28 cm.

Lit.
Roger-Marx, No. 25.

One of three lithographs commissioned for the paper *L'Escarmouche*. See Nos. 325-6. Toulouse-Lautrec also contributed to this paper.

Lent by the Bibliothèque Nationale, Paris

325
Garde Municipale 1893

Lithograph $6\frac{3}{4} \times 10\frac{1}{4}$ in./17×26 cm.

Lit.
Roger-Marx, No. 26.

See No. 324.

Lent by the Bibliothèque Nationale, Paris

326
Femme en Chemise 1893

Lithograph $6\frac{3}{4} \times 11\frac{3}{8}$ in./17×29 cm.

Lit.
Roger-Marx, No. 27.

See No. 324.

Lent by the Bibliothèque Nationale, Paris

327
La Grand'mère 1895

Lithograph $7\frac{1}{2} \times 8\frac{5}{8}$ in./19×22 cm.

Lit.
Roger-Marx, No. 30.

Plate for *L'Epreuve* (XI, XII).

Lent by the Bibliothèque Nationale, Paris

328
Poster for *La Revue Blanche* 1894

Lithograph $24\frac{3}{8} \times 31\frac{1}{2}$ in./62×80 cm.

Lit.
Roger-Marx, No. 32.

This monthly review, founded by the Natanson brothers, was first published in 1895. The *Revue* published in the same year an *Album*, containing lithographs by Bonnard, Vuillard, Lautrec and Roussel.

Lent by the Bibliothèque Nationale, Paris

329
Femme au Parapluie 1895
Lithograph 17⅜ × 8⅝ in./44 × 22 cm.
Lit.
Roger-Marx, No. 35.
Published in *L'Album de la Revue Blanche*.
Lent by the Bibliothèque Nationale, Paris

330
Nib Carnavalesque 1895
Lithograph 9⅞ × 12¾ in./25 × 32·5 cm.
Lit.
Roger-Marx, No. 36.
The *Nib*, published as a supplement to the *Revue Blanche* in 1895, only ran to three numbers. The verses are by Romain Coolus.
Lent by the Bibliothèque Nationale, Paris

331
La dernière Croisade (?) 1895
Lithograph 11¾ × 19¼ in./30 × 49 cm.
Lit.
Roger-Marx, No. 39.
Decoration for a theatre programme for a production at the Théâtre *L'Oeuvre*.
Lent by the Bibliothèque Nationale, Paris

332
La petite Blanchisseuse 1896
Lithograph in five colours 7½ × 11¾ in./19 × 30 cm.
Lit.
Roger-Marx, No. 42.
A plate for *Album des Peintres-Graveurs* (1).
Lent by the Bibliothèque Nationale, Paris

333
Poster for le Salon des Cent 1896
Lithograph in three colours 17¾ × 24¾ in./45 × 63 cm.
Lit.
Roger-Marx, No. 45.
Lent by the Bibliothèque Nationale, Paris

334
Complainte de M. Benoit *c.* 1898
Lithograph 9¼ × 12¼ in./23·5 × 31 cm.
Lit.
Roger-Marx, No. 49.
One of six title pages for poems by Franc-Nohain, set to music by Claude Terrasse. See also Nos. 335-339.
Lent by the Bibliothèque Nationale, Paris

335
La Berceuse obscène *c.* 1898
Lithograph 9⅞ × 12¼ in./25 × 31 cm.
Lit.
Roger-Marx, No. 50.
See No. 335.
Lent by the Bibliothèque Nationale, Paris

336
Paysage de Neige *c.* 1898
Lithograph 10¼ × 12¾ in./26 × 32·5 cm.
Lit.
Roger-Marx, No. 51.
See No. 335.
Lent by the Bibliothèque Nationale, Paris

337
Du Pays Tourangeau *c.* 1898
Lithograph 9⅞ × 12⅛ in./25 × 31 cm.
Lit.
Roger-Marx, No. 52.
See No. 335.
Lent by the Bibliothèque Nationale, Paris

338
La Malheureuse Adèle *c.* 1898
Lithograph 9 × 12⅛ in./23 × 31 cm.
Lit.
Roger-Marx, No. 53.
See No. 335.
Lent by the Bibliothèque Nationale, Paris

339
Velas ou L'Officier de Fortune *c.* 1898

Lithograph 9¾ × 12⅛ in./24 × 31 cm.

Lit.
Roger-Marx, No. 54.

See No. 335.

Lent by the Bibliothèque Nationale, Paris

340
Couverture de la *Lithographie en Couleurs* 1898

Lithograph in three colours 5⅞ × 8½ in./15 × 21·5 cm.

Lit.
Roger-Marx, No. 72.

La Lithographie en Couleurs by André Mellerio was published in 1898 for *L'Estampe et l'Affiche.*

Lent by the Bibliothèque Nationale, Paris

341
Screen 1899

Lithograph, four panels, each 53½ × 18¼ in./135 × 46·4 cm.

Coll.
Redfern Gallery, London.

Published by Molinas, 20 Rue Lafitte, in an edition of 110 (cf. Roger-Marx, No. 47). A distemper composition on unprimed canvas of the same theme, which can be dated *c.* 1892-94, belongs to a private collector, New York (cf. New York, 1964-5, No. 3).

Lent by Jeremy Hutchison, Esq.

342
Les Boulevards 1900

Lithograph in four colours 10¼ × 13 in./26 × 33 cm.

Lit.
Roger-Marx, No. 74.

Lent by the Bibliothèque Nationale, Paris

343
Poster for 'Le Figaro' *c.* 1904

Unique example, with drawings by the artist.

Exh.
Milan, 1955.

Lit.
Roger-Marx, No. 71.

Lent by Mm. Sagot-le-Garrec et Cie

344
Paysage du Midi 1925

Lithograph 8⅝ × 11⅜ in./22 × 29 cm.

Lit.
Roger-Marx, No. 82.

One of four lithographs for the album devoted to Bonnard in the series *Maîtres et Petits-Maîtres*, which was published in 1925 with a preface by Claude Roger-Marx.

Lent by the Bibliothèque Nationale, Paris

345
Les Bas 1928

Lithograph 8½ × 12 in./21·5 × 30·5 cm.

Lit.
Roger-Marx, No. 88.

Lent by the Bibliothèque Nationale, Paris

346
Femme assise dans sa Baignoire 1942

Lithograph in nine colours 9⅞ × 11⅜ in./25 × 29 cm.

Lit.
Roger-Marx, No. 78.

For a programme cover for a charity performance given by Maurice Chevalier at Cannes, 14th August 1942.

Lent by the Bibliothèque Nationale, Paris

347
Le Basset

Dry Point

Lent by the Bibliothèque Nationale, Paris

Books illustrated by Bonnard

Bonnard illustrated a number of books, of which a selection is exhibited here. For a complete list, see Rewald, p. 151.

348
Claude Terrasse: 'Petit Solfège Illustré'

Quantin, Paris, 1893.

Lent by a Private Collector, Paris

349
Peter Nansen: 'Marie'

La Revue Blanche, Paris, 1898.

Lent by a Private Collector, Paris

350
André Mellerio: 'La Lithographie originale en Couleurs'

Paris, 1898

Two coloured lithographs including the cover.

Lent by the Victoria and Albert Museum

351 *Page illustrated p. 30*
Paul Verlaine: 'Parallèlement'

Ambroise Vollard, Paris, 1900.

109 original lithographs.

Lent by the Victoria and Albert Museum

352
Longus 'Les Pastorales de Longus' or 'Daphnis et Chloë'

Ambroise Vollard, 1902.

Lent by a Private Collector, Paris

353
Octave Mirbeau: 'Dingo'

Ambroise Vollard, Paris, 1924.

55 original etchings.

Lent by the Victoria and Albert Museum

354
Pierre Bonnard: 'Correspondances'

Paris, 1944.

Facsimile autograph text of letters written by Bonnard as a young man, illustrated in pen and ink and pencil.

Lent by the Victoria and Albert Museum

355
Jules Renard: 'Histoires Naturelles'

Paris, 1945

Numerous pen illustrations.

Lent by the Victoria and Albert Museum

2　**House with a Tower** (**Near le Grand-Lemps**) *c*. 1888

10　**La Partie de Croquet** 1892

12　**Vue Panoramique** 1894

18　**Les Trois Poupées** 1895

28　**Canotage sur la Seine** *c*. 1897

7(a) **Femme à la Robe à Pois blancs** 1891   21   **Nu: Fond verdure** *c.* 1895

34   Chez la Brodeuse *c.* 1898

32   La Place Clichy 1898

26   Les Grands Boulevards *c.* 1895-1900

36   La Lampe à l'Huile 1898-1900

41   L'Indolente: Femme assoupie sur un Lit *c.* 1899

39   Interior: The Terrasse Children 1899

14   **La Rue en Hiver** 1894

15   **Figures dans la Rue** *c.* 1894

23   **La Lampe** *c.* 1895-96

37   **Le Repas** 1899

45 **Paris: Night** 1900

42 **La Marchande de Quatre Saisons** *c.* 1899

60   **Le Ruban rose** *c.* 1905

62   **Femme aux Bas noirs** *c.* 1905

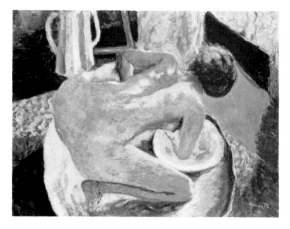

102   **Nu accroupi dans un Tub** 1912

49   **Thadée Natanson et jeune Femme** *c.* 1900-03

65   **Repas de Bêtes** *c.* 1906

66   **Sur le Yacht** 1906

46   **La Famille Terrasse, ou l'Après-Midi Bourgeoise** 1900

74   **Le Clocher** 1907

99   **Boulevard de Clichy** *c.* 1911

80   **Le Paon ou les Trois Grâces** 1908

81   **Fin de Repas au Jardin** 1908

89 **Siesta – The Artist's Studio** *c*. 1908-10

113 **The Regatta** *c*. 1913

98   **Paysage à trois Personnages et Saule** 1911

92   **The Blue Balcony** 1909-10

91   **Après le Deluge** 1909-10

118 **Still Life** 1914

87   **Young Girl reading** *c.* 1908

59   **Interior with Woman seated** 1905

90　**Nude** *c.* 1909

71　**Dans le Cabinet de Toilette** 1907

136　**Fenêtre ouverte à Uriage** 1918

128　**Nu debout** *c.* 1916-19

133   **L'Esterel** *c.* 1917

138   **The Abduction of Europa** 1919

158　**Monuments** 1921

129　**Symphonie Pastorale** 1916-20

156   **Portrait of the Artist** *c*. 1920-25

168   **Marthe Bonnard** *c*. 1923

167   **Portrait of the Artist** *c*. 1923

147   **Terrace at le Cannet** *c.* 1920

186   **Après le Déjeuner** *c.* 1925

154   **Levrette et Nature Morte** *c.* 1920-25

180   **Nature Morte à la Lumière du Soir** *c.* 1925

192   **Paysage, Vu des Toits** *c.* 1926-30

178   **La Fenêtre** 1925

241 **Nude in Yellow (Le grand Nu jaune)** *c.* 1938-46

100

233 **Nu à la Chaise** *c.* 1936-38

243 **Le Gant de Crin** 1939

238 **Nu à la Baignoire** *c.* 1938-41

213 **Femme nue au Gant** *c.* 1932-35

208　**Nu à la Baignoire** *c.* 1930

239   **Paysage: La Maison Rouge** *c.* 1938-41

249   **Paysage, Couchant; Le Cannet** *c.* 1943

254   **View from the Artist's Studio, Le Cannet** *c.* 1945

229   **La Prairie Fleurie** *c.* 1935

228   **Paysage vert** *c.* 1935

242 **L'Atelier du Peintre au Cannet** ('**Le Mimosa**') *c.* 1938-46

244 **Avant Midi: Le Cannet** *c.* 1939-45

121 **La Porte Ouverte** *c.* 1914-20

251 **Le Cannet: Paysage au Toit Rouge** 1944-45

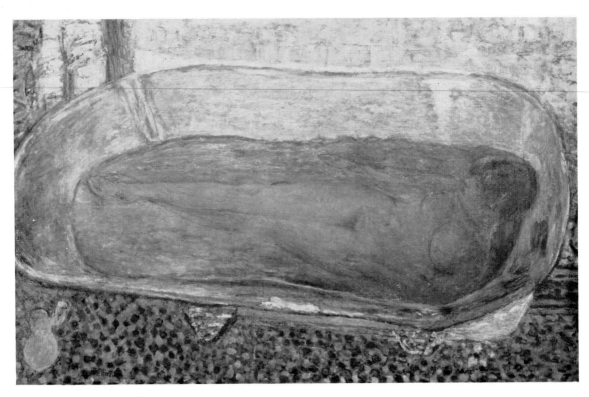

240 **La Baignoire** *c.* 1938-41

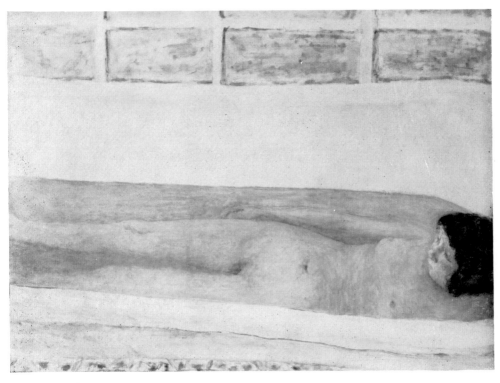

177 **Baignoire** 1925

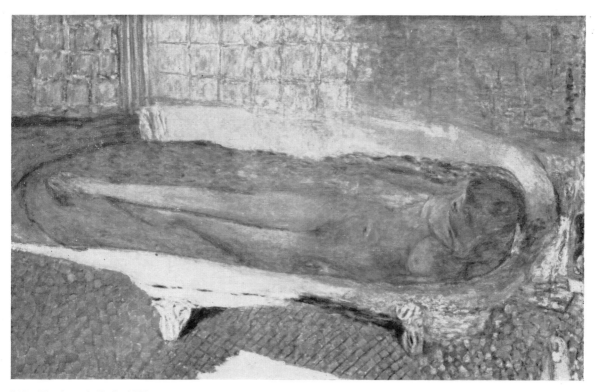

219 **Nu dans le Bain** 1935

237 **Nu dans la Baigncire** *c.* 1938-41

223 **Nature Morte** *c.* 1935

203 **Nature Morte** 1930

235 **La Cafetière** *c.* 1937

247 **L'Oiseau bleu** *c*. 1942-43

182   **Bateaux blancs** *c*. 1925

194   **Bords de Seine** *c*. 1928-30

232   **The Yellow Boat** *c.* 1936-38

230   **La Baie de Saint-Tropez** 1936

224   **Seascape at Cannes** *c.* 1935

216   **Le Boeuf et L'Enfant** *c.* 1934-46

234   **Cheval de Cirque** *c.* 1936-45